THE HISTORY OF THE
ROYAL BOTANIC
GARDEN LIBRARY
EDINBURGH

*One of Robert Kay Greville's drawings for the 'Plant scenery of the World' which he and John Hutton Balfour
planned to, but did not publish. The scenery here depicted is of Sikkim (Himalaya). 26×17.5 cm.*

THE HISTORY OF THE
ROYAL BOTANIC
GARDEN LIBRARY
EDINBURGH

MANJIL V MATHEW

HMSO EDINBURGH

ISBN 0 11 493342 1

Préface

The library of the Royal Botanic Garden Edinburgh is the result of many fortunate episodes and a long series of beneficial collaborations. There is no great collected corpus of records of the library's history so the author, Mr Mathew, has pieced together the facts from many scattered sources. Against the odds he has done this so successfully that the result is a satisfying account of the continuous development from the early beginnings in the late seventeenth century.

What began as the personal library of the Regius Keepers and Professors of Botany has grown to be the most comprehensive library on taxonomic botany, horticulture and allied subjects outwith SE England. It complements the collections in the University of Edinburgh, the National Library of Scotland and the Royal College of Physicians of Edinburgh, so that together they are a totally competent resource for studies. Whereas before the mid-nineteenth century, the library was very much a minor resource, the very fortunate gift of the library of the Botanical Society of Edinburgh set a new standard—especially in running a worldwide exchange of periodicals. This development was further strengthened by Bayley Balfour's launching of the Garden's own publication *Notes from the Royal Botanic Garden Edinburgh*. The transfer of the Cleghorn Memorial Library from the Royal Scottish Museum considerably enriched the Garden's library.

In spite of the enormous increase in botanical publications the library has been able to maintain comprehensive coverage of its fields. Those who built so well in the early days would be fascinated to read Mr Mathew's unravelling of the story of the library and could feel pleasure that they founded a tool which is now an important part of the scientific heritage of Scotland.

PROFESSOR D M HENDERSON
Regius Keeper
Royal Botanic Garden, Edinburgh

15 August 1986

Acknowledgements

This History would not have been written but for the approval and encouragement of Professor D M Henderson, the Regius Keeper, Dr J Cullen, the Assistant Keeper and Mr A J C Grierson, the Library Supervisor to whom I am very grateful.

I thank the staff of the National Library of Scotland, Edinburgh University Library, Edinburgh Public Library, Scottish Record Office and the libraries of the Scottish Office, the Royal College of Physicians of Edinburgh, Royal Scottish Museum, Botany School, Oxford, Royal Botanic Gardens, Kew, and the British Museum (Natural History), London, for their help in answering enquiries and obtaining some of the original sources I needed to examine.

Among the many friends and colleagues who assisted me in one way or other I would thank particularly Mr B L Burtt for his unfailing encouragement and very useful comments on matters historical and bibliographical. I am especially obliged to my colleague in the Library, Mrs D A Morrison whose support was invaluable. My thanks are also due to Dr Mary Noble and Mr John Currie for reading the draft and making useful suggestions.

I also record my thanks to Dr Graham Jones of the School of Librarianship, University of Strathclyde, Glasgow, for steering me along throughout the writing-up of my thesis for the degree of Master of Arts which, in large part, forms the basis of this History.

My especial thanks are due to Dr Brian Coppins and Mrs Norma Gregory for their infinite patience in editing and preparing the text for press, to Mrs Sally Rae for drawing the map of Edinburgh and to Mr Ken Grant for preparing the photographs.

List of Illustrations

FIGURES

PLATES

Regius Keepers of the Gardens

HOLYROOD PALACE AND TRINITY HOSPITAL
James Sutherland (1639–1719)   *RK 1699*–1715*
William Arthur (d. 1716)   *1715*
Charles Alston (1685–1760)   *1716–1760*

TRINITY HOSPITAL AND LEITH WALK
John Hope (1725–1786)   *1761–1786*

LEITH WALK
Daniel Rutherford (1749–1819)   *1786–1819*

LEITH WALK AND INVERLEITH
Robert Graham (1786–1845)   *1820–1845*

INVERLEITH
John Hutton Balfour (1808–1884)   *1845–1880*
Alexander Dickson (1836–1887)   *1880–1887*
Isaac Bayley Balfour (1853–1922)   *1888–1922*
William Wright Smith (1875–1956)   *1922–1956*
Harold Roy Fletcher (1907–1978)   *1956–1970*
Douglas Mackay Henderson (1927–)   *1970–*

---

* This is the date of the Royal Warrant from William III; no earlier one has been found.

Library Personnel

SUPERVISORS OF THE LIBRARY

Brian Lawrence Burtt   *1951–1961?*

Douglas Mackay Henderson   *1961?–1970*

James A Ratter   *1970–1977*

Andrew J C Grierson   *1977–1984*

James Cullen   *1984–*

OFFICERS IN CHARGE OF THE LIBRARY

James McNab*   *Curator***   *1872–1876*

Frederick M Webb   *Superintendent***   *1876–1880*

Henry Hastings†   *In Charge***   *1890–1908?*

Harry Frank Tagg   *In Charge***   *1908–1912*

James Todd Johnstone   *Librarian*   *1912–1946*

Dorothea E Purves   *Librarian*   *1946–1955*

J Marguerite Alford   *Librarian*   *1955–1961*

William Hunter Brown   *Librarian*   *1961–1967*

Manjil V Mathew   *Librarian*   *1967–*

ASSISTANT LIBRARIANS

Hugh A Colquhoun   *1961–1966*

Agnes W Laidlaw   *1962–1963; 1963–1964; 1966*

Barbara Fairweather   *1967–1968*

Jean Wood   *1969*

Katherine S Milne   *1970–1971*

David Parker   *1971–1975*

Lynda Clark   *1975–1979*

Erica Baber   *1978–1979*

Deborah A Morrison   *1980–*

* *McNab was the first Curator of the Herbarium and Library of the Botanical Society of Edinburgh in 1836.*

** *Honorary positions.*

† *Hastings was Clerk to Isaac Bayley Balfour. He was placed in overall charge of the Library while other assistants acted as librarians on a rota basis, one week at a time.*

SITES OF THE ROYAL BOTANIC GARDEN EDINBURGH

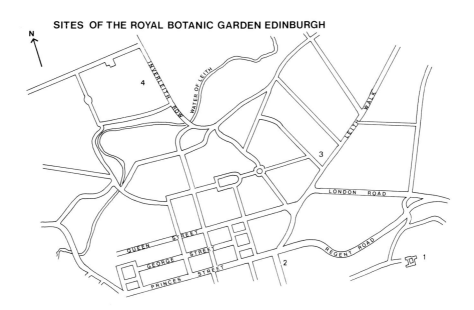

The plot of land in the North Yards of Holyrood Palace (location 1) where the Garden was started in 1670 soon proved too small for the purpose. Additional ground was therefore obtained near the Trinity Hospital (location 2) in 1675. Although the original Holyrood site was soon abandoned, in 1695 the King's Garden at Holyrood was taken over in addition to the Garden at the Trinity Hospital site. From 1746 onwards the importance of this second Holyrood site diminished while the Trinity Hospital site gained in status. The Garden was moved to Leith Walk (location 3) in 1763, and in 1820 it was transferred to its present site at Inverleith (location 4). The last move took some three years to complete.

1 Introduction

When Andrew Balfour and Robert Sibbald opened their Physick Garden in 1670 their aim was to provide the medical practitioners in the city of Edinburgh with a regular supply of medicinal plants. This aim was soon fulfilled. Sibbald said of this:

> By what we procured from Leviston and other gardens, and brought in from the Country, we made a collection of eight or nyne hundred plants ther . . . After this, we applied ourselves with more care to embellish the fabrick of the garden, and import plants from all places in this garden . . . and by Dr Balfour's procurement, considerable pacquets of seeds and plants were yeerly sent hither from abroad, and the students of medicine got directions to send them from all places they travelled to, wher they might be had, by which means the garden increased considerably every yeer.[1]

James Sutherland, the first 'Intendant' of the Garden, said in his catalogue of plants at the Garden: '. . . now it plainly appears that many of these SIMPLES that were wanted here, and therefore yearly brought from abroad, because of their Usefulness in Physick, may now by Industry and Culture be had in plenty at home'.[2]

Even as the collection of plants in the Garden was growing in number, the teaching of the virtues of simples and of botany conducted there was gaining importance and recognition. Initially the actual teaching was probably done by Sibbald and Balfour, Sutherland acting as demonstrator. Soon, however, Sutherland, too, began to give lessons at the Garden, which gained for him admission to the teaching profession in the Town's College. By 1695 the Town Council had created for him a Chair of Botany.[3] Referring to the teaching facilities offered by the Garden Sutherland said:

> And it is evident that the Apothecaries Apprentices could never be competently instructed in the Knowledge of Simples (which necessarily they ought to be) before the Establishing of theis garden; for now they may learn in one Summer, then formerly it was possible for them to do in an Age. And to make the thing easier for Beginners, I have planted in One Corner of the Garden, the Dispensatory Plants in an alphabetical Order. And for those whose Curiosity and Time gives them further desire of learning BOTANIE, I have disposed of whole Plants according to the most natural and rational Method, and according to the best and latest Authors of BOTANIE, and particularly our most Learned and incomparable countryman Doctor MORISON, by their GENERA and SPECIES; by means whereof, they come not only more easily to be known, but also much better retained in Memory, I have given the English Names as well as the Latin, that the Catalogue might be the more useful to all Persons; and especially those that are unskilful in the Latin.[2]

This teaching activity led to the establishment at the Garden of the Department of Botany of the University of Edinburgh, and the appointment of the Regius Keeper of the Garden as the Professor of Botany of the University as well.

Side by side with the growth of the Garden and the development of teaching, there was the work of classification and naming of plants—an essential feature of any collection of plants used for scientific study. Speaking of the arrangement of plants Sibbald was particular to mention that the classification adopted was that of the Swiss botanist Caspar Bauhin.[4] As mentioned earlier, Sutherland, too, gave much importance to this aspect of his work. This, known in scientific circles as Taxonomic Botany, has been a major concern at the Garden throughout its long history, and today it is its primary function.

A collection of the plants required for study is obviously a necessity for taxonomic work. Many botanical institutions go to great lengths to grow thousands of plants in their gardens. However, no garden, regardless of its resources, can grow within its confines all plants of all lands and of all climes. Nor is it really necessary. The purpose of taxonomic botany can easily be served without loss of efficiency or accuracy by plants collected in their natural habitats and preserved in herbaria as dried specimens or in other suitable ways.

Much botanical study and research is carried out today all over the world without the support of a large garden of living plants, and using specimens from one's own herbarium or borrowed from others. However,

> A herbarium without a library simply cannot function. It is not enough to have access to a large central library—the books must be housed in or immediately adjacent to the herbarium itself.
>
> Taxonomy is a science in which history plays a very important part. Hence it is essential to have on hand the literature on plants published during a period of about 300 years . . .[5]
>
> The science of taxonomy depends on the work of botanists who have published their observations and conclusions in books and periodicals. Without ready access to the relevant publications concerned with the geographical area in which he is working a botanist is severely handicapped. In fact, sound work cannot be attempted under these circumstances. A herbarium without a library may be likened to a ship without a crew . . .[6]

A library being so indispensable for taxonomic work, it would be surprising if the Royal Botanic Garden in Edinburgh had done without one for over 200 years and yet had maintained a reputation for the quality of its taxonomic work. It must have had a library prior to the arrival there of the books of the Botanical Society of Edinburgh in 1872. The Garden's account books show that at least from as early as 1766 books were purchased specifically for use in the Garden.[7] They were not many in number, but were standard taxonomic works of the period. Indeed, there was need for more books; this was satisfied by the library of the Regius Keeper in office.

The foundation of the Garden was an entirely private venture; it was not until the Universities (Scotland) Act of 1889 that complete responsibility for the Garden was taken over by the Commissioners of Her Majesty's Works and Public Buildings. The Act stated:

> From and after the first day of April one thousand eight hundred and eighty-nine, title, and interest of Her Majesty, Her Heirs and successors,

in right of Her Crown as proprietor of the Edinburgh Botanic Garden and all buildings therein, shall be vested in the Commissioners of Her Majesty's Works and Public Buildings, for behoof of the public, without prejudice to the rights of Her Majesty, Her Heirs and successors, as superior of the said garden and buildings, and to the rights of any subject superior in and to the said garden and buildings, the said garden and buildings be held by the said Commissioner of Her Majesty's Works and Public Buildings were acquired by or on behalf of His late Majesty King George the Fourth.[8]

Until this time maintenance and development of the Garden was the responsibility of the person in charge. In the early days Sutherland had the active support of the two founders. But soon he was left to his own resources which were mainly his wage supplemented by the fees he collected from the students who received instruction from him at the Garden and the gifts he 'obtained of money from the Exchequer, and the Lords of Session and Faculty of Advocates . . .'[1] These were far from adequate for the procurement of new plants, especially from abroad, purchase of garden implements, erection of greenhouses, hot-houses and fences, paying for assistants' wages and ground rent, not to mention the buying of books necessary for the classification and naming of plants. The situation was no different during the periods of office of his successors. In fact, the history of the Garden is full of the constant struggle of the Regius Keepers to obtain funds for its advancement. They were not always successful. More often than not they had to spend their own money even to buy new plants. What chance did they have to get funds to buy books? What they could buy from the grants received, they bought, as seen from the account books; the rest they bought themselves.

As long as Balfour and Sibbald were actively involved in the affairs of the Garden, their large libraries were freely available to anyone who wished to use them. By the time Sutherland left the Garden he had a sizeable library. Likewise his successors. These libraries were as much part of the Garden as the plants there, but paid for by the Regius Keepers from their own pockets and hence their property, to be removed at will.

Removing plants, particularly well established trees of some 40 years growth, is not the easiest of tasks. So no Regius Keeper attempted it. The widow of Charles Alston (Regius Keeper of the Garden from 1715–1760) was fortunate that she received some compensation for leaving her husband's plants in the Garden (see Appendix 1), but other more easily removable items such as books which belonged to the Regius Keepers were removed from the Garden when they retired from, or died in, office, leaving there only those which were bought from garden funds, and possibly a few from the Keepers' libraries. However, over the years, many hundreds of books which were at the Garden at one time or other as part of the then Regius Keeper's library have returned there, including at least one which belonged to Sutherland. Thus today the stock in the library at the Royal Botanic Garden in Edinburgh forms a perhaps fragile, but continuous chain back to the days of its foundation in 1670.

As noted above the Regius Keeper of the Garden was also the Professor of Botany of the University. Among the responsibilities and rights attached to his latter position was the provision of library facilities for his students.

Records of the Edinburgh University Library show that at least from the time of Alston books were bought for the use of students of botany.

Included in the Medical Faculty was the Chair of Botany, certainly from the time of Charles Alston, who was Professor of Botany from 1738 to 1761. Alston was opposed to Linnaeus's system; it was too new for him to accept. His successor John Hope was however an apostle of Linnaeus, and this conversion of botanical teaching to the new system is certainly reflected in the borrower's register for 1767, when Linnaeus's works were the more frequently borrowed on the subject. Lee's AN INTRODUCTION TO BOTANY and Hudson's FLORA ANGLICA were also popular. It is perhaps not entirely coincidental, either, that the list of medical purchases for 1762 includes no fewer than five works by Linnaeus. We should beware of drawing too close a connection between the appointment of John Hope and the Library Purchases, since we do not have Library records prior to 1762, and therefore cannot claim that no works by Linnaeus were purchased before then. However, the sheer number of Linnaeus accessions in this year suggests a filling in of gaps in the Library holdings.[9]

In 1826, His Majesty's Commissioners, taking evidence at the University of Edinburgh, asked Dr Robert Graham, the then Regius Keeper and Professor of Botany, not if there was a library, but: 'Is the library sufficiently supplied with books in your department of study?' to which Graham replied: 'Very inadequately indeed.' The next question was: 'Have the students easy access to such books as are in the library?' And Graham answered: 'I do not think the attendants at the library are sufficiently numerous, and the students are consequently frequently detained too long in getting books. Every facility, however, is given that the present attendants can give.'[10]

That was ten years before the Botanical Society of Edinburgh was even founded. Possibly such criticism of the library of the Botany Department enabled the Professor of Botany to exert pressure on the University Library to buy more books for the Botany Department. John Small the University Librarian told the Universities (Scotland) Commission in 1876: 'The botanical department [alone] would swallow up nearly the whole of our funds.'[11]

There was therefore, a library at the Garden from its earliest days, composed of the Garden's own books, the libraries of the Regius Keepers, and the departmental library of the University. It is the history of these libraries which this book proposes to trace. It is also the purpose of this study to mention a few of the more rare and valuable items in the library, and to describe the library as at the time of writing.

NOTES AND REFERENCES

1. SIBBALD, Robert: Life of Sir Robert Sibbald, Knight, MD, written by himself, 1695, In MAIDMENT, James (ed.) (1834). Analecta Scotica . . . Edinburgh, ch. XLIX, pp. 136–137.

2. SUTHERLAND, James (1683). Dedication in Hortus Medicus Edinburgensis: a catalogue of the plants in the physical garden at Edinburgh . . . Edinburgh.
   SIMPLES are plants and herbs employed for medical purposes.

3. FLETCHER, Harold R and BROWN, William H (1970). *Royal Botanic Garden Edinburgh 1670–1970*. Edinburgh, HMSO, p. 12.

4. SIBBALD, Robert (1684). *Scotia illustrata . . .* Edinburgh, Pars secunda . . . ch. II, p. 65.

5. FOSBERG, F Raymond and SACHET, Marie-Helene (1965). *Manual for tropical herbaria.* Utrecht, International Bureau for Plant Taxonomy [*Regnum vegetabile* Vol. 39], p. 83.

6. WOMERSLEY, J S (1981). *Plant collection and herbarium development . . .* Rome, FAO [FAO Plant production and protection paper 33], p. 84.

Other people, too, have emphasised the importance of a good library for taxonomic work:

> Taxonomy is fundamentally a descriptive and highly documented science. For this reason its literature is voluminous and constitutes so vital a part of its structure that, irrespective of whether the problem is one of identification of an unknown plant, solution of a nomenclatural puzzle, or a monographic or floristic study, acquaintance-ship must be made with the more important publications of the subject. (LAWRENCE, G H M: *Taxonomy of vascular plants.* New York, Macmillan, 1963, ch. XIV, p. 284).

> . . . Taxonomic descriptions are required to conform to certain rules and, in turn, must be referred to in subsequent studies of the same or similar organisms. The international rules of nomenclature lay down the essential requirements which, for example in botanical practice, include Latin descriptions of families, genera and species. Furthermore, in establishing the correct application of a particular name, taxonomists must refer to the original description and type specimens and often also to earlier works on related taxa, at times as far back as Linnean descriptions of the 18th century. Thus, taxonomic papers which contain descriptions of new species and/or revisions of families or genera, are of lasting importance to be referred to by future taxonomists. (SMITH, Eric (*Chmn*) *Taxonomy in Britain*; report by the review group on taxonomy set up by the Advisory Board of Research Councils . . . London, HMSO, 1979, ch. 5, p. 20, para. 546).

7. MS and typescript transcript of the Pipe Rolls and accounts of the Royal Botanic Garden, Edinburgh, 1764—(In the RBG Library, Edinburgh).

8. Universities (Scotland) Act, 1889, para. 24.

9. SHEPHERD, Christine (1982). The inter-relationships between the library and teaching in the seventeenth and eighteenth centuries. *In* GUILD, Jean R and LAW, Alexander (eds) *Edinburgh University Library 1580–1980; a collection of historical essays.* Edinburgh, University Library, p. 80.

10. *Evidence, oral and documentary, taken and received by the Commissioners appointed by His Majesty George IV, July 23rd, 1826 and re-appointed by His Majesty William IV, October 12th, 1830; for visiting the Universities of Scotland,* Vol. 1. University of Edinburgh . . . London, HMSO, 1837, p. 264.

11. Quoted by: SIMPSON, S M: History of the library 1837–1939. *In* GUILD, Jean R and LAW, Alexander (eds) (1982). *Edinburgh University Library 1580–1980; a collection of historical essays.* Edinburgh, University Library, p. 99.

2 The Physick Garden and its Founders

The standard of medical practice in Edinburgh in the second half of the seventeenth century bore no resemblance to that on the continent. While Leyden and Paris were making great forward strides in the method and technique of treating diseases, Edinburgh was still stagnating in the ignorance and quackery of earlier years. Nor was any concern about this expressed by the leaders of the community. This was all too obvious and deeply disturbing to those in the town who had travelled and trained abroad in medicine and related fields. Two such were Andrew Balfour and Robert Sibbald. Public spirited and vigorous as they were, they wanted to improve these conditions. Being men of some standing and influence in the town they were able to start a Physick Garden where as many as possible of the simples required in the practice of Physic could be grown and made available. They leased a small plot of land, not more than 40×40 ft, in the North Yard of Holyrood Palace, and assembled there some eight or nine hundred plants from the garden of their late friend, Patrick Murray, Laird of Livingston, and from the garden of Balfour himself. This was the beginning of the present Royal Botanic Garden in Edinburgh.[1] The year was 1670.

The venture was an entirely private matter for Balfour and Sibbald. But it had, and was seen to have, important consequences to the town's people, and more particularly to the medical fraternity, who understandably felt threatened and believed that their livelihood was at stake. Their suspicion and even resentment were soon allayed and their opposition turned into active support. Before long, the Town Council, the Exchequer, the Lords of Sessions and the Faculty of Advocates contributed money towards the up-keep of the Garden.[2] These occasional grants helped Balfour and Sibbald defray the expenses of the Garden during the first few years when they were actively involved in its management. They were, however, busy men, with greater interests and deeper commitments elsewhere which prevented them from devoting all the time and effort the Garden demanded. Their role, therefore, soon became limited to acting as official Visitors to the Garden, an office to which they were appointed by the Town Council,[2] and to exercising their influence to obtain new plants for the Garden. So, James Sutherland, who the founders had placed in charge of the Garden, soon found himself very much responsible for its maintenance and development. His financial resources were not princely. His income from an annual salary of £20 plus the money received from the students in return for his teaching at the Garden was far from sufficient to pay the ground rent and meet all the other expenses. Grants received from different sources did help, but did not form a dependable regular income. The first Treasury endowment was not made until 1763, and it was a century and a quarter later that the Universities (Scotland) Act of 1889 made the Garden a responsibility of the Crown.[3]

It is important to bear this in mind because only in the light of this can the early part of the history of the Library at the Garden be fully appreciated. Notwithstanding the periodic grants received, particularly to pay off the serious debts the Garden often incurred, the financial responsibility for the Garden's maintenance and development was entirely on the Keeper. Even as he was responsible for the provision of plants and all other necessary amenities, he was also required to provide a library from his personal financial resources. This was the situation at the Garden from the time of Sutherland, the first Keeper, to the time of Robert Graham who died in office in 1845.

One important consequence of this state of affairs was that the Garden was considered, quite rightly, the property of the Keeper, because all its contents were largely paid for from his own pocket. Naturally, he was free to take away with him all that belonged to him, when he retired from office, or if he died in office, his heirs had the right to them. That this was the case is clearly seen from the events following the death in office of Charles Alston in 1760, and immediately after the arrival, as the Keeper, of John Hope in 1761. Alston was at the Garden for over 44 years, and during this long period in office he had implemented considerable improvements, but with little financial assistance. At the time of his death he had no money left for the support of his widow and daughter, because he had spent it all on the Garden. Mrs Alston wanted to sell the plants in the Garden to support herself and her daughter. But she was prevailed upon not to do so, and when John Hope came on the scene, he caused Mrs Alston to petition the Treasury for financial compensation for the plants she was prepared to leave in the Garden. Her petition was favourably considered and she was duly compensated. (See Appendix I.)

It is, therefore, clear that although the plants and other improvements were part and parcel of the Garden, they were still the property of the Keeper, and accepted as such by all concerned. It was fortunate that the successive Keepers did not exercise their right to remove plants from the Garden when they left. In any case it would have been virtually impossible for a private individual or his family to remove fully grown and well established trees from one garden to another, especially if the resources available were meagre. But books were different: they were easily removed, and disposed of. This was what happened with the libraries of all Keepers of the Garden from Sutherland to Graham. Their libraries which were as much part of the Garden as the plants and other improvements there, were removed at the end of their term of office, and in most cases auctioned, the proceeds going to the families concerned. Extant documents show that all Keepers of the Garden kept libraries of their own, and they were open for use by anyone. These libraries left the Garden with their owners at various times. But, as has already been said, several of the books which were at the Garden at one time or another as part of the then Keeper's library, and hence of the Garden, have come back to the Garden in later years, including at least one from Sutherland's library, and also the entire botanical library of John Hope, thus forming an unbroken chain from Sutherland to the present day.

ANDREW BALFOUR

During the early years of the Garden, its founders, Andrew Balfour and Robert Sibbald, were actively involved in all matters relating to it and its management; financial responsibility for its maintenance and development mostly rested with them. It was up to them to provide the books necessary to identify, name and classify the plants and to ascertain their medicinal properties and uses. This was no particular problem for either of them, because both had not only magnificent libraries of their own, but extensive museums of antiquarian curiosities from many lands and climes. It was said of Balfour's library and museum:

> He brought with him the best library, especially in medicine and natural history, that had till then appeared in Scotland; and not only these, but a perfect knowledge of the languages in which they were written; likewise many unpublished MSS of learned men: A series of antique medals, modern medallions and pictures and busts, to form the painter and the architect: The remarkable arms, vestments, and ornaments of foreign countries: Numerous mathematical, philosophical, and chirurgical instruments, which he not only possessed but used; with operations in surgery, till then unknown in this country: A compleat cabinet, with all the simples of the materia medica, and new compositions in pharmacy; and large collections of the Fossils, Plants and Animals, not only of the foreign countries he traversed, but of the most parts of the world.*

> These treasures of learning, imported into a country where the like had not been formerly seen, made a considerable figure, and drew the eyes of all who had any taste for letters. But they were not so much designed for show, by the proprietor, as for use. It was not a mere rage for collecting, that put him to so much labour and expense. These valuable materials for the purpose of medicine and natural history, he dedicated through his whole life, as he did at last, to the service of the public.[4]

> Of a liberal and communicative disposition, his library, his museum, and his intructions, were open to all who had the merit to avail themselves of the advantage.[5]

> His library and museum were forty years work, of unremitted attention.† For their better accommodation, he built an addition to his house , when he had arrived at near his sixtieth year; but after the building was completed, he became so infirm as to be unable to put them in that order which he intended.

> After his death, his library, consisting of about three thousand volumes, besides manuscripts, was sold, of which there is a printed catalogue that still remains.[6]

*Mem. Balf. pp. 63–67. The whole plants preserved in his travels, bound in several volumes, were in his museum after it was placed in the College of Edinburgh. Mem. p. 53. But this collection, which would now be of great value, has since disappeared.[4]

†In his library, he had always many duplicates of rare and valuable books for the gratification of his friends, and colleagues. At a visit paid him by the Duke of Lauderdale, in which the conversation turned upon the Greek classics, he presented the Duke with some of the most ancient scholiasts upon the Greek Poets, which the latter had not been able to procure. Sibbald.—Mem. p. 67[6]

The auction catalogue (Fig. 1) of Balfour's library[7] listed over 3,500 titles of printed works and manuscripts, divided into groups of subjects and languages, and each group further divided into groups by the size of the books. The library contained important collections on a variety of subjects, including the humanities, literature, philosophy, mathematics, theology, etc. The largest collection was on medicine which included pharmacy, chemistry, anatomy, surgery, botany, and natural science, and contained almost 1,500 titles. Sibbald spoke particularly highly of Balfour's MSS collection, enumerating some of them, and adding that it contained: 'Also some books from China and from other places in the East Indies, collections of maps, plans of ancient buildings, engravings of famous men, mathematical and surgical instruments, microscopes, collections of animals, minerals, products of the sea, rare plants, woods, fruits, gums.'[8]

Balfour himself did not publish any books during his life time. However, in 1700 his son published, anonymously, a collection of letters Balfour had written to Patrick Murray before the latter had set off to the continent in search of plants. It was: *Letters Written to a Friend by the Learned and Judicious Sir Andrew Balfour, M.D. Containing Excellent Directions and Advices for Travelling thro' France and Italy . . . Published from the Author's Original MS. Edinburgh, 1700.*

The auction catalogue of Balfour's library carried an advertisement which said: 'There will be shortly ready for the Press, *Memoria Balfouriana*, or a Historical Narration of the Life and Death of *Sir Andrew Balfour, M.D.* written in Latine by *Sir Robert Sibbald, M.D.* together with Epitaphs in several Languages.'[7] The book was published in 1699.[8]

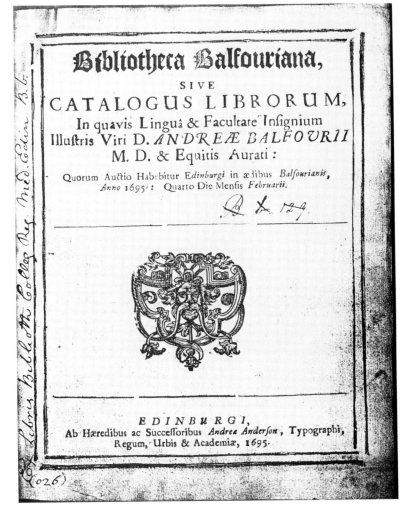

1. Title page of sale catalogue of Andrew Balfour's Library. 21.5 × 16.5 cm.

Balfour left most of his important manuscript collection to his friend and co-founder of the Garden, Robert Sibbald,[9] who was an even greater collector of books and manuscripts. He said of himself: 'From the tyme I entered to the Coledge, any mony I gott, I did imploy it for buying of books.'[10] Unlike Balfour, Sibbald published a number of works, and many of the books he purchased were for use in the writing of his books. 'This', said Sibbald, 'was the cause of great paines and very much expence to me, in buying all these books

2. Title page of sale catalogue of Robert Sibbald's Library. 20×14.5 cm.

Bibliotheca Sibbaldiana:

OR, A

CATALOGUE

OF

Curious and Valuable BOOKS:

Consisting of

Divinity, Civil and Ecclesiastical History, Medicine, Natural History, Philosophy, Mathematicks, Belles Lettres, &c.

WITH

A curious Collection of Historical and other Manuscripts.

Being the Library of the late Learned and Ingenious Sir ROBERT SIBBALD of KIPPS, Doctor of Medicine.

To be Sold by Way of Auction, on *Tuesday* the 5th of *February*, 1723, at his House in the *Bishop's-Land* in *Edinburgh*; where Placards will be affix'd.

The Time of Sale is to be from Two of the Clock to Six in the Afternoon.

The BOOKS *may be seen Eight Days before the Auction.*

CATALOGUES are to be sold for a Sixpence each, at *William Brown's*, and most of the Booksellers Shops in *Edinburgh*, and at the Place of Sale.

EDINBURGH, Printed in the Year M.DCC.XXIII.

and manuscripts I could gett for that use, and procuring information from all parts of the country, even the most remote Isles. I employed John Adair for surveying, and did bestow much upon him, and payed a guinea for each double of the Mapps he made.'[11]

Balfour and Sibbald were among the founders of the Royal College of Physicians of Edinburgh, which received the Royal Charter in 1681, and of which Sibbald was elected President in 1684. Balfour and Sibbald were knighted in 1682. In the same year Sibbald presented to the College a small collection of books. 'I gave about this tyme a presse with three shelfs full of books, to the College of Physitians, amongst which were Galen's works, 5 volumes Greek, and five Latine, Hippocrates in Greek, of Aldus' edition, Gesner his history of animals, 3 volumes, Paris bind, and some other valuable books.'[12] This was the beginning of the present vast and very valuable library of the Royal College.

After Sibbald's death in August 1722, his library was sold by auction in February 1723. The auction catalogue (Fig. 2) of his library[13] listed nearly 5,500 works, printed and manuscript, and was arranged in the same style as that of Balfour. Medical and natural history books were the more numerous, with just under 1,600 titles. There were 1,486 works on Scripture, 951 on Theology, almost 1,200 on Geography and well over 100 valuable manuscripts. 'Most of the MSS. and many of the printed books, were bought by the Faculty of Advocates. The total amount of the purchase came to £342. 17s. Sterling—a very large sum in those days. It was with considerable difficulty that this purchase was effected, as a number of the members of faculty violently opposed it.'[14] 'Sum of all the MSS. £260.0s.0d.'[15] All of these, along with the considerable library of the Advocates, were presented to the Scottish Nation in 1925 to form the foundation of the National Library of Scotland.

The large libraries of Balfour and Sibbald were the first two libraries to which the Physick Garden had access for the execution of its business of organising and making use of its plant collection. Much as in the case of the later libraries in the Garden, these did not belong to the Garden, and yet were part of the establishment, as long as their owners were in charge there.

NOTES AND REFERENCES

1. SIBBALD, Robert: Life of Sir Robert Sibbald . . . written by himself, 1695. In MAIDMENT, James (ed.) (1834) Analecta Scotica . . . Edinburgh, ch. XLIX, p. 136.

2. Ibidem p. 137.

3. FLETCHER, Harold Roy and BROWN, William Hunter (1970). Royal Botanic Garden Edinburgh 1670–1970. Edinburgh, HMSO, pp. 59, 202–203.

4. WALKER, John (1808). Essays on natural history and rural economy. Edinburgh, pp. 353–354.

5. Ibidem p. 357.

6. Ibidem pp. 364–365.

7. Bibliotheca Balfouriana, sive catalogus librorum . . . Andreae Balfourii . . . Edinburgh, 1695.

8. SIBBALD, Robert (1699). *Memoria Balfouriana, sive historia rerum* . . . *Fratribus Balfouriis, D D Jacobo* . . . *et D D Andrea* . . . Edinburgh, p. 65. (Translation by Emeritus Prof. A G Morton).

9. STEPHEN, Leslie (ed.) (1885). *Dictionary of National Biography,* vol. 3. London, p. 49.

10. SIBBALD—Ref. 1 above, p. 130.

11. SIBBALD—Ref. 1 above, pp. 142–143.

12. SIBBALD—Ref. 1 above, p. 148.

13. *Bibliotheca Sibbaldiana:* or, a catalogue of curios and valuable books . . . being the library of . . . Sir Robert Sibbald . . . Edinburgh, 1722.

14. SIBBALD—Ref. 1 above, p. 159 footnote.

15. Note in manuscript, at the bottom of p. 140 in the copy of Ref. 13 above, originally of the Advocates' Library, and now in the National Library of Scotland.

3 The Libraries at the Trinity Hospital Site, 1675 - 1763

JAMES SUTHERLAND

The early history of the Royal Botanic Garden in Edinburgh and the lives and achievements of its early Regius Keepers and Principal Gardeners were the subject of considerable research by Sir Isaac Bayley Balfour, Regius Keeper from 1888 to 1922, and Dr John Macqueen Cowan, Assistant Keeper from 1930 to 1954. In the case of James Sutherland, the first Regius Keeper of the Garden, Daniel William Kemp, the reputed author of many works on matters relating to Sutherlandshire, contributed a great deal of additional information from his own research. The results of all these investigations, which have been published in the *Notes from the Royal Botanic Garden, Edinburgh*, reveal but little about Sutherland's early life.[1] All that can be said about it is that he must have been in Edinburgh for at least some time when Andrew Balfour and Robert Sibbald started their Physick Garden in the city. Sibbald tells us: 'We had, by this tyme, become acquaint with Master James Sutherland, a youth, who, by his owne industry, had attained great knowledge of the plants and of

3. *Title page of James Sutherland's Catalogue of plants . . . 16.5×10.5 cm.*

4. *Note attached to one copy of Sutherland's Catalogue in the Library. The date, 1861, is well before the arrival of the Botanical Society Library at the Garden.*

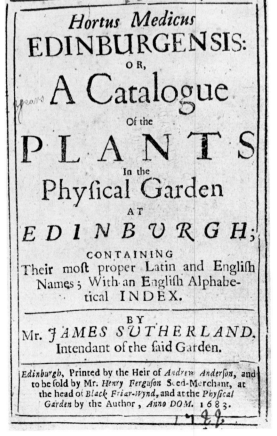

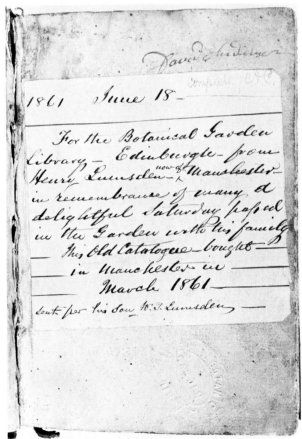

medals'.[2] He also tells us that he and his colleagues interested in promoting botanical studies, having taken up the subject of the Physick Garden began to consider the laying out and equipping of a medical garden in Edinburgh 'especially when Mr James Sutherland was offering his aid in tending the plants. This gentleman was a most learned botanist, and a capable man of business, (which latter fact commended him to Balfour in no small degree)'.[3]

There is no doubt about Sutherland's knowledge and industry because, under his care, the Garden soon developed into one of the finest in the country, and its fame spread on to the continent. His *Hortus medicus Edinburgensis: or, a catalogue of the plants in the Physical Garden at Edinburgh*, 1683, (Figs 3, 4) is eloquent testimony to his excellent achievements in the Garden. In the Epistle Dedicatory of his Catalogue, Sutherland claimed:

> I dare boldly say, comparing it with the CATALOGUES of gardens abroad, it runs up with most of them, either for Number, or Rarity of Plants: it having been my Bussiness these seven years past, wherein I have had the Honour to serve the City as Intendant over the Garden, to use all care and Industry by forraign correspondence to acquire both seeds and plants from THE LEVANT, ITALY, SPAIN, FRANCE, HOLLAND, ENGLAND, EAST AND WEST INDIES . . .

This 'forraign correspondence' must have brought in a fair number of other garden catalogues with which Sutherland could compare his own. He was not, however a collector of seed and plant catalogues alone. In order to understand the habitats and habits of foreign plants, the uses, medicinal and otherwise, they could be put to, and the requirements for their successful cultivation in the climate of Scotland, he needed books which dealt with such matters. More importantly perhaps, he needed to refer to standard works on existing systems of plant classification and nomenclature to help him identify, name and classify the plants coming into the Garden from different parts of the country and from abroad, and plant them in the most useful order, with their English as well as Latin names, for the best advantage of the students and others frequenting the Garden.[4] He had access to the large libraries of both Balfour and Sibbald, and he also received books from them and other friends.[5] That did not dissuade him from acquiring many books of his own. As early as 1676 the Town Council considered this as a necessary part of his job and recommended 'to the thessr [treasurer] of the Colledge to provyd a conveenient roome in the Colledge for keeping books and seeds relating to the said profession'.[6] Early the next year the Council again 'recommends to the said thessr to provyd a convenient roome in the Colledge for the better keeping and preserving of such books, Seeds -c. as are necessarie and the key thereof to be kept be the sd. Mr. Sutherland and his successores in office'.[7]

The Town Council's recommendations throw up some interesting points for consideration. Obviously they were speaking to the College treasurer from their position of authority over the College. Their clear recommendation was to provide Sutherland with a room in the College where he could keep his books. It may be that Sutherland was not, in 1676, a Professor of the College. Nevertheless, the previous year he had been appointed a salaried 'Intendant' of the Garden with teaching responsibilities, and this profession had been 'joined with to' the other professions taught in the Town's College.[8] Sutherland was thus a member of the teaching profession at the College, admittedly below the position of Professor. This position which he held in the College must have influenced the Council's recommendations.

The Town Council's own efforts to enhance the stock of the main College Library in those early days were largely through inducement and encouragement of donations and bequests.[9] The earliest class or departmental libraries were supplied with books by the professors of the departments concerned and the students themselves, or by private subscription.[10] There is no evidence that the Town Council granted any money to Sutherland for the purchase of books which he was to keep in a room in the College. As the other professors did for their respective departments, Sutherland bought books for his 'department'. As mentioned earlier, some books were given him by friends. Looking at it in this light, Sutherland's library was the earliest class or

5. First page of Robert Eliot's Hortus Siccus. 31×22 cm. (see Appendix X— ELIOT, Robert)

departmental library of the University of Edinburgh, pre-dating by some 20 years or more the Theological Library founded in 1698.[10]

That Sutherland was to keep the key to the room was possibly for the security of the seeds etc. which were also there. But that recommendation deprived William Henderson, the then College Librarian, of all control over the books. The Town Council's inclusion of Sutherland's successors in office in their recommendations suggests that they expected the library to remain in the College. This was, however, not to be. Termination of Sutherland's connection with the College in 1706 was not under the happiest of

6. *The cabinet in which Sutherland's 'Medals' were kept.*

circumstances.[11] Very likely he took the library with him when he left. It is known that in the previous year he 'made a donation of all his medalls with his books on yt subject to ye faculty of Advocates for qch they are obleidged to pay him yearly during life a salary of 50 lib. st; and to be keeper of them'.[12] The rest of his books were donated to the Advocates' Library early in 1707.[5] The sale of duplicates in the Advocates' Library in 1707 included some of Sutherland's books. One was a copy of the incunable, the 1485(?) *Latin Herbarius*, which having passed through different libraries was bought for the Library at the Royal Botanic Garden in Edinburgh, in 1900, at the auction of the library of James Hardy of Old Cambus.[13]

The Advocates' Library sold Sutherland's coins with the cabinet (Fig. 6) which housed them, to the Society of Antiquaries of Edinburgh in 1872. 'The price paid to the Faculty of Advocates for the collection of coins and the cabinet was £783, 12s, of which £50 was taken by both parties as the sum applicable to the cabinet'. Within a few years the cabinet was thought to be probably of the time of Louis XV and offers to purchase it began to be made.[14] In 1881 it was sold for £3,500. *The Scotsman* reported it as 'A windfall for the Antiquarian Museum', describing the circumstances which led to the sale.[15]

The interesting point relating to this history is that the Advocates' Library sold only the coins and medals which they had received from Sutherland. There is no mention of the books being sold to the Society of Antiquaries. It is reasonable to assume that the Advocates retained the books, and gave them to the Scottish nation in 1925 along with their entire library, to form the foundation of the present National Library of Scotland.[16] However, the list of Sutherland's books in the National Library, compiled by William A. Kelly of that library, does not mention many on coins and medals.[5] Perhaps Sutherland had only a few books specifically on numismatics, but rather more on antiquities and curiosities in general. This is supported by the contents of Kelly's list. It contained over 300 titles, some in duplicate, the majority, as one would expect, herbals, other early works on physick and botany and works on plant distribution, description and classification as known at the time. There are no less than twelve works by Caspar Bauhin in the list. Other works by botanical authorities are also well represented and there are works on natural history, including zoology, travel, and one particularly interesting copy of William Daniel's Irish New Testament of 1602.[17]

In 1706 Sutherland was obliged to resign his College posts but continued to be Regius Keeper and King's Botanist at the Royal Garden until 1715. Charles Preston and his brother George succeeded Sutherland in the College posts from 1706 to 1711 and 1712 to 1738 respectively.[18] Neither of them had any official connection with the Royal Garden. Their history, therefore, is of little relevance here. Nevertheless, it is interesting to note that at the time of his death in 1711 the larger part of Charles Preston's estate was his library: 'his whole books and pamphlets valued by Alex Henderson bookseller in Edinburgh to the sum of £90 11sh. Scots money'.[19] This was, perhaps, another early class library of the College.

WILLIAM ARTHUR

The person who succeeded Sutherland at the Royal Garden in 1715 was William Arthur. He did not make any impression at all in the Garden because he stayed in office only for a very short time. He was an extreme Jacobite and had to flee the country after the failure of the 1715 Rising. He died in Rome in 1716 'from eating figs'.[20]

CHARLES ALSTON

For all practical purposes, therefore, Sutherland's real successor at the Royal Garden was Charles Alston, appointed in 1716. He had no responsibilities to the College where the Prestons were in office until 1738. When George Preston retired from the College in that year Alston was appointed to the post,

7. A page from Charles Alston's MS of his lectures. 19×12 cm.

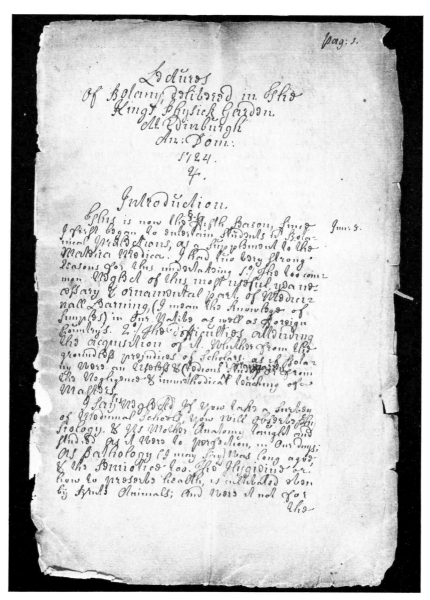

thus coming to hold all the positions which Sutherland held at the height of his career, principally those of Regius Keeper and King's Botanist at the Royal Garden, and Professor of Botany at the College. This tradition continued for well over two centuries when, in 1956, the two posts of Regius Keepership of the Garden and Regius Professorship of the University were separated.[21]

Alston remained at the Garden for 44 years. He was an excellent teacher, published several works and carried on an extensive correspondence with a number of leading botanists of the time. He is, however, remembered particularly for his trenchant opposition to the then new sexual system of plant classification introduced by the Swedish botanist Carl Linnaeus. Despite the increasingly wide acceptance of the new system by many, Alston remained opposed to it all his life.[22, 23]

It was suggested that this was the reason for Alston perhaps not recommending the purchase of many of Linnaeus's works for the University Library.[24] However, for Alston to have been able to refute the Linnaean arguments he must first have known what those arguments were from the published works. Either he bought the books himself or they were sent to him by friends. There is evidence of both. Alston was a subscriber to Sebastien Vaillant's *Botanicon Parisiense . . .* which Hermann Boerhaave edited and published in Amsterdam in 1727.[25] Possibly he was also a subscriber to the *Philosophical Transactions of the Royal Society of London.* Philip Miller promised to send a copy of the abridgement of his *Gardener's Dictionary* to Alston. A copy of Johann Jakob Dillenius's *Historia Muscorum . . .*, 1732, was sent to him by his friend John Fothergill. Several other papers and prints were also sent to Alston by various people. Many of the letters Alston received suggest a continuing review by Alston of the works being published at the time.[26] This he could not have done without seeing the books themselves.

Alston thus had a library of his own, and it must have been of some considerable size. Besides this, there was the library of the University to which he had rights and responsibilities as the Professor of Botany and of Materia Medica. As in the case of his predecessor Sutherland, and those of his successors Hope, Rutherford and Graham, Alston's library was removed from the Garden after his death and sold by auction in February 1761.[27] Fortunately the Garden Library today possesses several of Alston's published works and manuscripts (Fig. 7) left at the Garden at the time as being of little monetary value. The Library also has transcripts of most of Alston's correspondence, the originals of which are in the Edinburgh University Library.

A typescript biography of Alston by a descendant of his is deposited in the National Library of Scotland. A copy of it is in the Royal Botanic Garden Library, Edinburgh.[28]

NOTES AND REFERENCES

1. The archival collection at the Royal Botanic Garden Library in Edinburgh contains a large number of items relating to the early history of the Garden, its Keepers and Principal Gardeners. Comprising printed and manuscript material, both in original and transcript, these were gathered principally by Isaac Bayley Balfour, J M Cowan and D W Kemp, over a number of years, and form a considerable primary source for the history of the Garden to the last few years of the nineteenth century.

Bayley Balfour's brief sketches of the Regius Keepers appeared in the preliminary pages of the many early volumes of *Notes from the Royal Botanic Garden, Edinburgh*, except volumes 9–12, under the title 'Historic notice'. A more expanded version appeared in: Oliver, F W (ed.) *Makers of British Botany*, CUP, 1913, pp. 280–301, under the title 'A sketch of the Professors of Botany in Edinburgh from 1670 until 1887'. His biography of William Arthur was published in *Transactions of the Botanical Society of Edinburgh* 1915, vol. 26, pp. 375–404. A full account of the early Principal Gardeners was published in *Notes from the Royal Botanic Garden, Edinburgh* 1904, vol. 3, pp. 17–374. When Bayley Balfour knew that D W Kemp was researching the life and work of James Sutherland, he handed over to Kemp the materials he had collected himself and offered all help for further research and final writing of Sutherland's biography by Kemp which would be published in the Garden's *Notes*. The research proved to be long and difficult and it was 1912 before Kemp had his biography of Sutherland ready for the press. Kemp wanted a facsimile of Sutherland's *Hortus Medicus Edinburgensis*, 1683, to be issued with the biography. Balfour's own idea was a less expensive reprint of the *Hortus* . . . with anotations as necessary, giving modern names of plants. However,

> . . . the Stationery Office has recently had a fit of economy, and characteristically, instead of tackling large outlets of expenditure has fixed upon our small outgo for our 'Notes' as a field for the exercise of its retrenching zeal, and I have not yet come to an understanding—although I have the support of my Board—with the Stationery Office in the matter of the publication of Sutherland's catalogue. The Stationery Office has represented that it is a matter upon which public funds should not be spent . . .
>
> In discussing the question of publication with the Stationery Office the question was raised as to the number of copies likely to be sold of the completed account in view of the necessity of fixing a price for the volume which would bring back some return to the Stationery Office for its outlay in printing. Have you any information that would enable you to say what market there is for a book of this kind? If I had such information it would help me in completing arrangements with the Stationery Office for publication . . . (Bayley Balfour's letter dated 12 January 1912 to D W Kemp).

The work was not published as planned. It was several years later that J M Cowan re-examined the research papers of Balfour and Kemp, added his own research and published a well documented *History of the Royal Botanic Garden, Edinburgh*, in *Notes from the Royal Botanic Garden, Edinburgh*, 1933–35, vol. 19, pp. 1–134. It dealt with the early history of the Garden, Sutherland and the Prestons.

2. SIBBALD, Robert: Life of Sir Robert Sibbald, . . . written by himself, 1695. *In* MAIDMENT, James (ed.) (1834). *Analecta Scotica* . . . Edinburgh, ch. XLIX, p. 136.

3. SIBBALD, Robert (1699). *Memoria Balfouriana* . . . Edinburgh, p. 69. [In Latin].

4. SUTHERLAND, James (1683). Epistle dedicatory, in *Hortus Medicus Edinburgensis*, Edinburgh.

5. FACULTY OF ADVOCATES. Records of the clerk of the Faculty, Ref. FR 139: Mr Jacobus Sutherland horti Redij ad Coenobium Sanctae Crucis praefectus libros qui sequuntur ad botanicam, historiamque naturalem dono dedit. X Kal. Martijs Anni 1707.

These books, now in the National Library of Scotland, have been listed by William A Kelly of that library (unpublished typescript). This list mentions books presented to Sutherland, and books which once belonged to Andrew Balfour and Robert Sibbald.

6. EDINBURGH TOWN COUNCIL. Records, vol. 28, f. 182, 8 Sept. 1676 (Quoted by J M Cowan in *Notes from the Royal Botanic Garden, Edinburgh*, 1933, vol. 19, p. 15).

7. *Ibidem* f. 215, 5 Jan. 1677 (Quoted by Cowan; see Ref. 6 above).

8. COWAN, John Macqueen (1933). In *Notes from the Royal Botanic Garden, Edinburgh*, vol. 19, p. 14.

9. FINALYSON, C P and SIMPSON, S M: History of the library 1580–1710. *In* GUILD, Jean R and LAW, Alexander (eds) (1982). *Edinburgh University Library 1580–1980* . . . Edinburgh, p. 51.

10. BELL, Margaret D: Faculty and class libraries. *In* GUILD, Jean R and LAW, Alexander (eds) (1982). *Edinburgh University Library 1580–1980* . . . Edinburgh, p. 164.

11. EDINBURGH TOWN COUNCIL: Records, vol. 38, f. 352, 29 Aug. 1705 (Quoted by Cowan; see Ref. 6 above, pp. 54–55).

12. Letter of Charles Preston to Sir Hans Sloane, dated in Edinburgh on 11 Sept. 1705 (Quoted by Cowan; see Ref. 6 above, p. 52).

13. Notes in manuscript and typescript in the copy of *Latin Herbarius* in the library at the Royal Botanic Garden, Edinburgh read:

> Ex Libris Bibliotheca Facultatis Juridica Edinbrugi 1707. Prius M. Jacobi Sutherland Advocates Library Duplicates Acquired for the Library of the Royal Botanic Garden, Edinburgh, in 1900 at the dispersal of the Library of the late James Hardy, Old Cambus.

> The present copy wants the title, the preface & the 1st leaf. Latterly it had belonged to Mr James Sutherland. the first Keeper of the Edinbr. Botanic Gardens; afterwards to the advocates Library; & then disposed of as a duplicate to C. Kirkpatrick Sharpe, the antiquary. I bought it from Mr. Alex Irvine, author of the "London flora", "British Flora" etc. The work had been in Scotland at an early period & has the names attached in the Old Scots language. Dates in the book of former owners 1517, 1523, 1529, 1582. On the last leaf there is a prayer for the safety of James Earl of Moray, regent of Scotland, 1567–1570. "God keep in gud hale & prosper. the thrice noble and mighty Lord James Earl of Moray Governor of the North & South of Scotland" The writing wh. follows refer to lucky and unlucky days, & may be an attempt to construct a horoscope, to fortell the events of a man's future in life, a practice not unfrequent in that age.

For additional information on the book, see:
a. HARGREAVES, G D (comp.) (1976). *A catalogue of medical incunabula in Edinburgh libraries*. Edinburgh, p. 29, no. 54.
b. ARBER, Agnes (1912). *Herbals* . . . Cambridge, Cambridge University Press, pp. 16–18.
c. ANDERSON, Frank J (1977). *An illustrated history of herbals*. New York, Columbia University Press, pp. 82–88.

14. Proceedings of the Society of Antiquaries of Scotland, 11 April 1881—Sale of Coin cabinet for £3,500 and Memorial of the Society of Antiquaries of Scotland to the Lords Commissioners of Her Majesty's Treasury (Transcript in the RBG Library, Edinburgh).

15. *The Scotsman*, Tuesday, 12 April 1881.

16. TAIT, James A and TAIT, Heather F C (comp.) (1981). *Library resources in Scotland, 1980–1981*. Glasgow, p. 67.

17. The inclusion of this volume in Sutherland's library may seem extraordinary until one considers that there was no translation into Scottish Gaelic of the New Testament until 1767, 48 years after his death. There is no evidence that Sutherland was either Gaelic-speaking or of Highland descent, but speakers of Scottish Gaelic were dependent on the Irish translation of the Bible before the publication of the Scottish Gaelic New Testament (1767) and Old Testament (1783–1801).

This particular volume is the first translation into Irish or Scottish Gaelic of any part of the scriptures and was made by William Daniel or O'Donnell, Bishop of Taum. Printing began in 1602 and it was published in Dublin in 1603 with a dedication in English to James VI and I. It is printed in Irish script, using types presented in 1571 by Queen Elizabeth, and was reprinted in 1679 by Robert Boyle. No Irish translation of the Old Testament was published until Boyle printed Bishop Bedell's translation in 1686 (Bedell was an Englishman who learned Irish when he was sixty): two copies of this were sent to the Highlands but Sutherland evidently did not acquire one. Versions of Roman script of the Irish Bible were made for use in the Highlands by the Rev. Robert Kirk and published in 1690: Kirk's Bible came into general use in Scotland, replacing the versions in Irish script, so Sutherland's copy of Daniel's New Testament is comparatively rare. The covers of his copy are worn and the spine has been replaced, but the good condition of the pages suggests that it was not Sutherland's favourite reading.

Further details of the Irish and Scottish Gaelic translations of the Bible are given in Rev. Donald Mackinnon's *Gaelic Bible and Psalter*, Dingwall, 1930. (I am grateful to Alisoun Morton, MA, MLitt, Edinburgh, for this comment.)

18. COWAN, John Macqueen (1935). History of the Royal Botanic Garden Edinburgh. *Notes from the Royal Botanic Garden, Edinburgh*, vol. 19, pp. 54–56, 64–120.

19. EDINBURGH COMMISSARIOT OF REGISTER OF TESTAMENTS. Will of Preston, 23 Jan. 1712 (Quoted by Cowan; see Ref. 18, p. 74).

20. BALFOUR, Isaac Bayley (1915). William Arthur, MD Botanist to the King in Scotland 1715–1716. *Transactions of the Botanical Society of Edinburgh*, vol. 26, pp. 375–404.

21. FLETCHER, Harold Roy and BROWN, William Hunter (1970). *The Royal Botanic Garden, Edinburgh 1670–1970*. Edinburgh, HMSO, pp. 40, 256.

22. *Ibidem* pp. 37–45.

23. Perhaps the antipathy between Alston and Linnaeus had something to do with their personalities. Alston believed himself to be the grand old man of botany:

> Doctor Alston, who is well known to have been many years one of the Professors of Medicine in the University of EDINBURGH, teaching in the winter, that branch of the science called MATERIA MEDICA, and in the summer, BOTANY; the cultivation of both which parts of medical knowledge has been the principal study of his life. His great natural abilities, learning, universal knowledge, sagacity, accuracy, candour, caution, solid judgment, indefatigable industry, inventive investigation, ardent love and steady pursuit of truth, and sacred regard for the public emolument and utility, joined to that tempering sweetness of disposition, which is very predominant in him, have enabled him by a long course of experience in practice, experiments and observations on natural bodies, much speculation, reading, deliberation and reasoning, to make useful improvements and discoveries, and detect egregious errors in the two above mentioned provinces of medicinal art, than which parts of medicine none are more fundamentally beneficial and entertaining and yet none have been hitherto less studied and less improved. His most elegant Dissertation on OPIUM, in the EDINBURGH MEDICAL ESSAYS, Vol. V. Part I, that on QUICK-LIME and LIME-WATER, his INDEX MEDICAMANTORUM TRIPLEX, and the subsequent treatise taken from his TIROCINIUM BOTANICUM EDINBURGENSE, are cofessedly substantial proofs of his shining talents and merit, and do him so great honour, that the learned vehemently desire and impatiently expect to see published by him a larger work, of which some of these less performances may perhaps be looked on as detached parts. I hope the Professor will pardon me for attempting to delineate a rude portrait of his illustrious endowments; which, though it is neither equal to the original, nor reconcileable to his delicate modesty, may shew my personal esteem of him, and that gratitude to him, for the benefit I have reaped from his already published tracts, which is a debt of common justice.

(This quotation is from the preface of Alston's *A dissertation on botany*, 1754, where he speaks of himself through a 'translator' who was Alston himself. *See* Pulteney, Richard (1790). *Historical and biographical sketches of the progress of botany in England . . .*, vol. II, p. 12.)

Linnaeus, also, thought much of himself:

> I have been doctor, professor, royal physician, knight and nobleman.
> I have been vouchsafed to see more of the Creator's wondrous works, in which I have found my greatest joy, than any other mortal who has lived before me.
> I have had my disciples sent out to the four corners of the earth.
> I have written more than anyone else now alive; 72 of my own books are at present on my desk.
> I have won a great name extending to the Indies themselves, and have been acknowledged as the greatest in my science.
> I have become a member of almost all scientific societies; in Upsala, Stockholm, Petersburg, Berlin, Vienna, London, Montpellier, Tolosa, Florence and now recently in Paris, with honourable mention among the 8 renowned men of the world . . .

(This quotation is from: Hagberg, Knut (1952). *Carl Linnaeus*, London, p. 206. Translated from the Swedish by Alan Blair.)

24. SHEPHERD, Christine: The inter-relationship between the library and teaching in the seventeenth and eighteenth centuries. *In* GUILD, Jean R and LAW, Alexander (eds) (1982). *Edinburgh University Library 1580–1980 . . .* Edinburgh, p. 80.

25. LINDEBOOM, Gerrit Arie (1968). *Hermann Boerhaave; the man and his work.* London, footnote on p. 147. The statement needs to be examined because the name which appears in the list of subscribers in the copy of the *Botanicon* . . . in the RBG Library is 'Edward Aston'. Boerhaave always addressed Alston as 'Carlos Aston' in his letters. The name 'Aston' may, therefore, be accepted for 'Alston'. But the name 'Edward' is puzzling. Perhaps Boerhaave did not know the first name until later, or, Lindeboom might have had other evidence to say that Alston of Edinburgh was a subscriber to the work mentioned.

26. Letters to Alston from John Hawkeens dated 19 Dec. 1741, 16 Feb. 1742 and 29 Nov. 1742; from John Fothergill dated 11 Sept. 1738 and 18 July 1741; from Philip Miller undated; from Stephen Hales dated 4 May 1756; from Alexr. Garden dated 16 Feb. 1756. Alston's letter to Philip Miller dated 16 Feb. 1756. (Transcript copies of these and many other letters are in the RBG Library, Edinburgh.)

27. *Edinburgh Evening Courant*, Saturday January 24, 1761. Advertisement on p. 2, col. 3, top.

> On Monday the second of February, begins to be sold by auction, at the house in the East wing of the new Exchange,
> A large collection of Medical and Botanical Books, being the library of the late Dr Charles Alston professor of Botany in the University of Edinburgh . . . Catalogues . . . to be had at the shop of G Hamilton and J Balfour, who will execute commissions . . .

A similar advertisement appeared in the same paper dated Saturday January 31, 1761, which specified 'THE BOTANICAL AND MEDICAL PART of the LIBRARY of the late Dr. Charles Alston . . .'

28. ALSTON, J M. Charles Alston, MD 1685–1760, Professor of Medicine and Botany at Edinburgh. (Typescript i–iv, 106 pp., 1980.)

JOHN HOPE

With the arrival of Dr John Hope in 1761 the Garden entered a new era of development. A pupil of Alston, Hope was as staunch an advocate of the Linnaean system of plant classification as his professor had been an adversary of it. He is regarded as partly responsible for the general acceptance of the system in British botanical circles.[1]

In 1763 Hope succeeded in obtaining a larger and better site for the Garden in Leith Walk as well as an annual grant of £119. 3s. from the Treasury. Receiving a grant obviously necessitated the keeping of proper accounts of expenditure. These accounts for the period of Hope and his successors clearly

8. *Title page of John Hill's Vegetable System. Qto. edn. 26×19 cm. (see Appendix X—Hill, John)*

THE

VEGETABLE SYSTEM.

OR,

A SERIES OF

EXPERIMENTS, and OBSERVATIONS

TENDING TO EXPLAIN

The INTERNAL STRUCTURE, and the LIFE of PLANTS;
their GROWTH, and PROPAGATION;

The NUMBER, PROPORTION, and DISPOSITION of their CON-
STITUENT PARTS; with the true COURSE of their JUICES;

The FORMATION of the EMBRYO, the CONSTRUCTION of the SEED,
and the ENCREASE from that State to PERFECTION.

INCLUDING

A NEW ANATOMY OF PLANTS.

The WHOLE from NATURE only.

By JOHN HILL, M.D.

LONDON:
Printed at the EXPENCE of the AUTHOR,
And Sold by R. BALDWIN, in Pater-Noster Row.
MDCCLIX.

show that books were bought from garden funds specifically 'for use of the garden' at least from 1766 onwards. On 15 December of that year a copy of Miller's *Gardener's Dictionary* (7th edition) was bought for £1. 8s. On 5 January of the following year £1. 9s. was spent on Linnaeus's *Genera Plantarum* and *Species Plantarum*. Another Miller's *Gardener's Dictionary* (8th edition) was purchased on 22 October 1768 for £3. 10s. This 8th edition was particularly needed in the Garden for the naming of plants because for the first time Miller had used binomial nomenclature for plant species; the 7th edition adopted the Linnaean system of classification, but not his binomials. In the same year a copy of Linnaeus' *Systema Naturae* was bought for 11s.[2]

Books were also purchased from garden funds to send to botanists abroad in exchange for plants and seeds received from them. Among those who thus received books from Hope were Francis Guthrie in Russia, William Roxburgh in Madras, John Lindsay in Jamaica and Archibald Menzies in Halifax, Nova Scotia.[2]

Edinburgh University Library records give ample evidence that, as Professor of Botany, Hope purchased books from the University's library fund.[3] One of Hope's letters to J E Smith speaks of the books he wanted to be purchased for the University Library.[4] The same letter and at least one other speak of the books Hope was interested in personally.[5]

Hope's own private library was not as extensive or as comprehensive in scope as those of Balfour and Sibbald. It nevertheless contained much of what was of significance to the study of botany and medicine of the time.[6] Hope allowed the use of his library by those who could benefit by it. William Smellie (1740–1795), the Edinburgh printer and naturalist whose name is closely linked with the publication of *Encyclopaedia Britannica*, in an undated letter to a friend said that Hope 'offered me the full use of his library'.[7]

When Hope died in 1786 his heirs took away his library and other papers except copies of some of Hope's own published works, some manuscript notes, illustrations and charts used at his lectures at the Garden. Unlike the libraries of his predecessors, however, Hope's library was not sold, but kept in the family for over a hundred years. When Hope's son, Thomas Charles Hope, who was Professor of Chemistry at the University of Edinburgh died in 1844, his library was added to that of his father. On the death of Hope's grandson, John Hope, in 1899, all botanical and related books from the entire library were handed over to the Botanic Garden Library by the Hope Trustees according to the instructions in the will of John Hope which read:

> . . . I hereby commend to the favourable consideration of the said Trustees their handing over in gift as aftermentioned, free of legacy duty, whichever of the books on botany, however many, belonging formerly to my grandfather, Doctor John Hope, and to my uncle Doctor Thomas Charles Hope, and now to me, may be selected by the Professor of Botany in the University of Edinburgh, at the time of my death, the same to be handed over, should the said Trustees decide to give them either to the University of Edinburgh or to any library connected with the Botanical Gardens in Edinburgh, whichever of these the said Professor shall select with the approval of the said Trustees.[8]

About 220 titles were thus received in the Garden. Some books which were missing from the collection at the time were later found among Hope's other effects and the Trustees promptly sent them to the Garden. Isaac Bayley Balfour who received the Hope books in the Garden was proud of the 'old Masters' added to the Library and considered 'The catalogue by Sutherland of plants in the Botanic Garden is a very precious possession'.[9] Among the books was a copy of Andrea Cesalpino's *De Plantis Libri XVI*, Florence, 1583, to the fly-leaf of which is attached a leaf carrying a note, unsigned, but in John Hope's handwriting: 'This very rare and long wished for Book was given to me in a present by Dr. Cullen 29 May [17]80'. Morton records that: 'The donor was probably William Cullen, Professor of Chemistry, and later of Medicine, at Edinburgh 1755–88'.[10] Scores of other books also bear Hope's autograph, and several have Hope's distinctive bookplates (Fig. 9) fixed to the covers.

At least part of Hope's herbarium was left at the University at the time of his death. It lay totally neglected until 1840 when it was amalgamated with the large herbarium of the Botanical Society of Edinburgh, and eventually in 1863 the whole herbarium was moved to the Garden.[11-15] Along with this came also some papers relating to the herbarium. Among them was the recently discovered original description and drawing of *Cinchona brachycarpa* (=*Exostemma brachycarpum*) sent to Hope in 1784 by John Lindsay from Jamaica (Fig. 10). These were reported lost in 1791.[16]

Hope's books and papers in the Library contain several volumes of manuscript notes taken by Hope's students at his lectures in the Garden. One

9. *John Hope's book plate. 6×5.5 cm.*

of them bound in a Persian style (Plate 6) has a bookplate (Fig. 11), and a manuscript note in the front with the name of Alex Boiswell appearing at the top of the page:

These notes were taken by me at the Botanical Garden Edinburgh in Summer 1780. In a voyage to India in 1785 Mr. Boiswell, then my mate who remained in the country had by mistake put them up in his trunk and lost them at the affair near Satimungulum where they were taken by

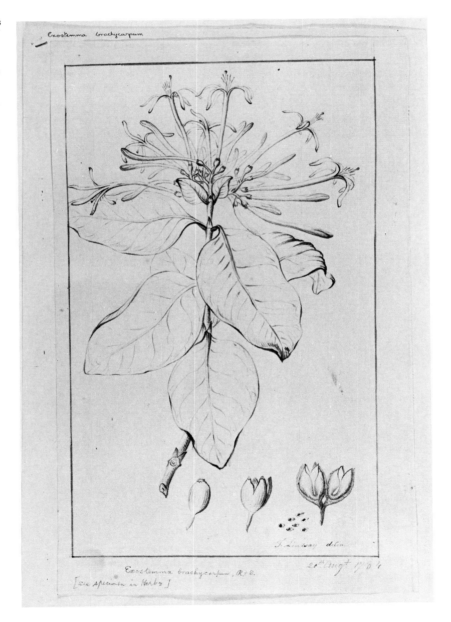

10. John Lindsay's original drawing of Cinchona sent to John Hope from Kingston, Jamaica, in 1784.
32×20 cm.
(see Appendix X—
LINDSAY John)

Tippoo, and by him bound up in their present form. At the taking of Seringapatam they fell into the hands of Major Ogg who restored them to me.

Francis Buchanan

Seringapatam 23 May 1800

Francis Buchanan, later Francis Buchanan Hamilton, was a statesman and botanist who spent several years in India. He held high office including that of Superintendent of the Botanic Garden in Calcutta. At the time of his death in 1829 in Leny, Scotland, he was Chief of the Clan Buchanan.

Hope's other papers, botanical and others, are now in the Register House in Edinburgh.[17] They are mostly in bundles with a contents list on top of each. Among the loose papers is a list of contents which mentions a 'History of Abbey Garden', but the history itself is not to be found among the papers. There is also a letter which Robert Freer wrote on behalf of Lady Hopetown to Hope. In it is said: 'Lady Hopetown appeared well pleased at your acct. of Mr Sibbald'.[18] These two items, if traced, may well throw more light on the early history of the Garden.

DANIEL RUTHERFORD

Daniel Rutherford, who succeeded John Hope in 1786, was basically a chemist, and at the time his interests in plants were only as objects for his experiments in chemistry. During his 33 years in office, he himself contributed but little to the advancement of botany or the development of the Garden. Nevertheless, the unerring judgement he used in the selection and appointment of a succession of excellent Principal Gardeners resulted in the Garden holding its place as a scientific institution and from the arrival of William McNab as Principal Gardener in 1810, the Garden developed into one of the finest of its kind in the world.[19]

As far as the Library is concerned, the Garden's account books of the period record the books that were bought, such as a copy of Lightfoot's *Flora Scotica*

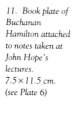

11. Book plate of Buchanan Hamilton attached to notes taken at John Hope's lectures.
7.5 × 11.5 cm.
(see Plate 6)

for 18s. 6d. on 26 January 1787 and another copy on 10 September. Aiton's *Hortus Kewensis* was bought for 2s. 3d. on 10 May 1793. These books must have been very heavily used, because, not long after their purchase, they had to be re-bound at 2s. 4d. for *Flora Scotica* and 2s. 3d. for *Hortus Kewensis*. Garden accounts have other entries for books purchased from booksellers such as William Creech and J Fairbairn, as well as for sums paid to bookbinders.[2]

Like his predecessors Rutherford too kept a private library. Judging from the value of £294. 9s. 9d. as assessed by the bookseller David Laing[20] at the time

12. Title page of Philipp Maximilian Opiz's Deutschlands cryptogamische Gewachse . . . *1816. 17×11.5 cm. (see Appendix X—OPIZ, Philipp Maximilian)*

of Rutherford's death in 1819, the library must have been of a respectable size. It was removed from the Garden by his daughter and sold by auction at the sale rooms of MacLachlan and Stewart of Edinburgh, in March 1820.[21] Some of Rutherford's botanical books have found their way back to the Garden in later years (Fig. 13) as donations by friends or through purchase.[22] The Library also has some manuscript botanical notes believed to be Rutherford's and copies of his published works.

13. Title page of Johan. Christoph. Wulff's Flora Borussica *which was in the library of Daniel Rutherford and now in the Garden Library. 20×11 cm.*

IOHAN. CHRISTOPH. WVLFF

MED. DOCT.

FLORA

BORVSSICA

DENVO EFFLORESCENS
AVCTIOR.

Cum Figuris.

REGIOMONTI ET *LIPSIAE*,

SVMTIBVS HAER. HARTVNG. ET IO. DAN. ZEISII.

MDCCLXV.

Malcolm McCoig (?–1789) and Thomas Sommerville (c.1783–1810), two Principal Gardeners at Leith Walk from 1782(?)–1789 and 1807(?)–1810 respectively, may be mentioned in passing in the context of libraries at Leith Walk.[23] McCoig was appointed by John Hope, but continued to work under Daniel Rutherford until 1789 when he died. In the inventory of his possessions prepared after his death were a considerable number of copies of many books.[24] Possibly he was a bookseller, or acted as agent to a bookseller or publisher in his spare time and sold books to students who attended lectures at the Garden.

Thomas Sommerville was appointed by Daniel Rutherford. The Garden needed much attention and Sommerville was beginning to make his mark when ill-health struck. Lingering for many months, he died in 1810, after only a very short active period in the Garden. The interest in Sommerville here is that he had a library of books and antiquarian objects in his house in the Garden. The content of the library was mostly botanical, but there were books on other subjects, particularly history. He also had the *Spectator*, 8 vols. with 'Names of the Authors, their Lives and Notes', and the *Rambler*, 2 vols. His library and other collections were sold by William Bruce in April 1810. A catalogue of the sale is still extant.[25]

NOTES AND REFERENCES

1. BALFOUR, Isaac Bayley: A sketch of the Professors of Botany in Edinburgh from 1670 until 1887. *In* OLIVER, F W (ed.) (1913). *Makers of botany* . . . Cambridge University Press, pp. 286–290.

2. Transcripts of these accounts are in the RBG Library, Edinburgh.

3. SHEPHERD, Christine: The inter-relationship between the library and teaching in the seventeenth and eighteenth centuries. *In* GUILD, Jean R and LAW, Alexander (eds) (1982). *Edinburgh University Library 1580–1980* . . . Edinburgh, University Library, p. 80.

4. Letter of John Hope to Sir J E Smith, dated at Edinburgh, 7 October 1784. *Extract:*
    . . . I thank you for Hedwig and Broughton, for wh. at meeting I shall pay you.
    . . . I have also to thank you for the list of Botanical Books you was so good as send me The following I wish purchased for the University Library but I beg you may not take further trouble than to put the List into the hands of Mr. Strachan bookseller, No. 70 Strand near Adelphi with such instructions as may be necessary. Curtis's Flora Londin. coloured No. 46 and all the following numbers . . . —As this copy is for the University Library I have flattered myself that Mr. Curtis paid attention to the choice of the numbers.
    Jacquin's Flora Austriaca, 5 vols.
    —Icones plantar rario. fol
    —Miscellanea Austriaca, 2 vol. 4to
    Schmidel's Dissertationes Botan. 4to
    Retzius Fascicul. Observ. Botan. 3 fascicul.
    Meerburgs Icones, Lugd. Bot.—
    Mr Strachan knows that the books for the Library cannot be paid till the books are lodged in it then they are instantly paid. I have all Schmidel's 50 plates but I have only 138 pages of the letter press—pray could I any how come to the rest of the letter press—I beg my kind compts. to Mr. Strachan. . . .
    Transcript in RBG Library, Edinburgh.

5. Letter of John Hope to J E Smith, dated at Edinburgh, 12 January 1784. *Extract:*
    . . . I was lucky enough to get a copy of Linnaeus's supplementum Plantarum. I wish I

could get Hedwig de muscis some time ago I recd. an Abstract of it in an inaugural dissertation wh. I think I showed you. I am impatient to see the 8 vol. of Amaenitates altho' I did not admire Linnaeus so much as a philosopher as a Naturalist and Systematist.

I sincerely lament the death of Linnaeus; it will be a severe blow to the progress of Botany and Zoology. We had reason to expect from him and speedily a new edition of the Genera and Species plantarum—I wish much to see Mr. Ayton's Hortus Kewensis. Linnaeus' premature death will render it much more neccesary and acceptable—when you see him pray remember me to him kindly . . .

Transcript in RBG Library, Edinburgh.

6. MS and typescript lists of books received at the Garden from the Hope Trust, 1899–1901. (In the RGB Library, Edinburgh.)

7. Typescript of this letter is in the RBG Library, Edinburgh.

8. This Extract, in MS, as sent by the Hope Trust, is in the RBG Library, Edinburgh.

9. Letter of Isaac Bayley Balfour to W M Ramsay (of the Hope Trust) dated 3 April 1901.

10. MORTON, A G (1981). *History of Botanical Science* . . . London, etc. Academic Press, p. 130 footnote.

11. Petition dated 30 July 1838 from the Council of the Botanical Society of Edinburgh, read at the meeting of the Society on 8 November 1838. (In the Minute Books of the Botanical Society of Edinburgh deposited in the RBG Library, Edinburgh.)

12. Letter dated 30 July 1838 from Professor Robert Graham to the Town Council of Edinburgh. (In the Minute Books as above.)

13. Report of the Committee of the Botanical Society of Edinburgh to the ordinary meeting of the Society on 10 January 1839. (In the Minute Books as above.)

14. Memorial dated 9 April 1863 from the Botanical Society of Edinburgh to the Commissioners of HM Office of Works. (In the Minute Books as above.)

15. HEDGE, I C and LAMOND, J M (eds) (1970). *Index of collectors in the Edinburgh herbarium.* Edinburgh, HMSO, pp. 3–4.

16. Paper of John Lindsay read at the meeting of the Royal Society of Edinburgh on 7 November 1791 and published in the *Transactions of the Royal Society of Edinburgh,* 1794, vol. 3, p. 211 and footnote. (See appendix 10, no. 8 and notes.)

17. Hope papers in Scottish Record Office, Register House, Edinburgh, Ref. GD 253 D & J H Campbell WS 143. Photocopies of all Hope's papers at Register House and at Edinburgh University Library are kept at the RBG Library, Edinburgh.

18. This letter, dated 25 July 1785, is among the Hope papers referred to in Ref. 17 above.

19. BALFOUR, Isaac Bayley: A sketch of the Professors of Botany in Edinburgh from 1670 until 1887. In OLIVER, F W (ed.) (1913). *Makers of Botany* . . . Cambridge University Press, pp. 290–291.

20. Extract of valuation of Rutherford's estate. (In the RBG Library, Edinburgh.)

21. *Edinburgh Evening Courant* 1820 Monday, 6 March (No. 16967), p. 3, col. 6:
This day is published, a Catalogue of the Library of the late Daniel Rutherford, M.D., Professor of Botany, in the University of Edinburgh, to be sold by auction, at the sale rooms of MacLachlan and Stewart, 62, South Bridge, Edinburgh on Monday the 13th March 1820, and on the eleven following lawful evenings precisely at six o'clock.

This Catalogue will be found to contain perhaps the most extensive and valuable collection of books (many of them with plates, beautifully coloured), on Botany and various branches of Natural History, ever offered for public sale in Scotland, together with many excellent editions of the Greek and Latin classical writers, with the most approved books on Medical Science, and of English Miscellaneous Literature.

The books for each evening's sale will be exhibited at the rooms from eleven till three o'clock in the afternoon. Catalogues to be had from MacLachlan and Stewart, and of William Laing, booksellers, Edinburgh.

Advertisements of the sale appeared in the same paper on March 13, 20 and 23. That of the 20th specified:

> . . . classics, Books on foreign languages, with Books of Prints, including the following:—
>
> Piranasi's large plates, and views of ancient Roman Architecture and Antiquity
>
> Spence's Polymetis, title impressions
>
> Banier's Ovid, with plates and Picart
>
> Bartoli's plates of the Antonini Column and of Roman Antiquities
>
> Gorge's Antiquities of Scotland, 2 vols. 4to
>
> Pennant's Tour in Scotland, 4to
>
> Johnson's English Dictionary, 2 Vols. folio original edition
>
> Bayle et Chaufepie, Dictionaire 9 Vols. folio in fine order.

> And the night of Wednesday, Thursday, Friday and Saturday, consist almost exclusively of an extensive and valuable collection of Books, relating to the Branches of Natural History and Botanical Science; many of these are finely coloured and are in excellent preservation but are too numerous for specification in an advertisement . . .

22. WULFF, Johann Christoph (1765). *Flora borussica denuo effiorescens autior* . . . Regiomonti et Lipsiae. The title page is autographed by D Rutherford (Fig. 13). The book came to the Garden in 1872, along with the Library of the Botanical Society of Edinburgh to which it was presented by Hugh Cleghorn in 1839.

23. BALFOUR, Isaac Bayley (1903–1908). History of the Royal Botanic Garden, Edinburgh. Principal Gardeners. *Notes from the Royal Botanic Garden, Edinburgh*, vol. 3, pp. 20, 291–292.

24. EDINBURGH COMMISSARIOT OF REGISTER OF TESTAMENTS (1789). Vol. 128, pt. 1. (Typescript in the RBG Library, Edinburgh.)

Extract of the Inventory of goods . . . belonging . . . to Malcolm McCoig, gardener at the Botanic Garden of Edinburgh in Leith Walk . . .

> Books, one hundred and fifty nine copies of the History and Progress of Botany in bundle first two shillings and six pence, one hundred and twenty copies of Genera Plantarum bundle second ten shillings, one hundred and nine copies of the Index Herbarium medicinalium bundle third two shillings and six pence, seventy nine copies of the Catalogus arborum et Fruiticum for the bundle, five copies of the Termini Botanici, fifth book, two shillings, twelve copies of the Plantarum officinarum seventh bundle . . .

25. *A Catalogue of Minerals, Fossils, Books &c. which belonged to the late Mr. Thos. Sommerville, manager of the Botanic Garden, Edinburgh. To be sold on Saturday April 28, 1810 at his house, Botanic Garden, Leith Walk, by Wm. Bruce Jun. The Sale to begin at 12 o'clock noon.* 8 pp. A copy of this catalogue is in the RBG Library, Edinburgh.

5 *The Libraries at Inverleith III, 1820-1887*

ROBERT GRAHAM

There was universal approval of Robert Graham[1] as successor to Daniel Rutherford, although the apparent haste with which the appointment was made displeased some. (Appendix II). Almost immediately after Graham took charge in December 1819 the decision was made to move the Garden from Leith Walk to Inverleith. It was a difficult task which took almost three years to complete. Once that job was done Graham was able to turn his attention to the development of the Garden and the University Department of Botany under his charge.

Before he came to Edinburgh Graham held the newly created Chair of Botany in the University of Glasgow, and in that capacity he played his role in the establishment of the Glasgow Botanic Garden in 1817. There was a room set aside at the Garden for botanical lectures. Also there was a Library as an integral part of its educational activities.[2] Obviously Graham considered a library a necessary adjunct to botanical instruction. When he came to Edinburgh, where botanical teaching was far in advance of Glasgow, he was not particularly happy about the state of the Library there. He did not have to wait too long before he could express his dissatisfaction. In 1826 he told His Majesty's Commissioners visiting universities in Scotland that the Library was very inadequate and its staff were not equal to the services expected by the students from the Library.[3] In that year Graham had 244 university students attending lectures in the class rooms at the Garden.

The inadequacy of the Library was made good, to some extent at least, by Graham's own library which he kept as up-to-date with books as his resources would permit. At the time of his death in 1845 it had some 400 books. It was sold by auction the following year by Messrs Tait and Nisbet, in Edinburgh, along with his very valuable herbarium.[4, 5]

Graham's greater service to the Garden Library was the part he played in the foundation and growth of the Botanical Society of Edinburgh. He was the first president of the Society and his enthusiasm and influence contributed largely to the great success of its activities and the building up of its herbarium and library. Graham himself donated some books to the Society's library. After his death, his widow presented to the Society a valuable collection of her husband's MS papers on botany.[6] All these, along with the library of the Society were gifted to the Garden in 1872.

JOHN HUTTON BALFOUR

John Hutton Balfour succeeded Graham in 1845. He was a student of Graham and was among the prime movers for the establishment of the Botanical Society of Edinburgh. Like his predecessor, he too was a keen supporter of the Society to achieve its

> aim for the promotion of Botany—amongst them the creation of a botanical library and herbarium. This has proved a signal service to

14. Frontispieces and title pages of the English edition of George Francis Hoffmann's Germany's Flora or a botanical pocket companion. 12.5×9 cm. (see Appendix X— HOFFMAN, George Francis)

GERMANY'S FLORA

OR

A BOTANICAL

POCKET - COMPANION

FOR THE YEAR 1791.

BY

GEORGE FRANCIS HOFFMANN.

ERLANG:

Printed for JOHN JAMES PALM, Bookseller,
and sold by B. WHITE AND SON, HORACE'S
HEAD, Fleet - Street, LONDON.

THE FLORA OF GERMANY

OR

A BOTANICAL

POCKET - COMPANION

FOR THE YEAR 1795.

VOLUME II.

CRYPTOGAMY

BY

GEORGE FRANCIS HOFFMANN
M. D. PROF. of MED. AND BOTANY
AT GOTTINGEN.

ERLANGEN,

Printed for JOHN JAMES PALM, Bookseller,
and sold by B. WHITE AND SON, HORACE'S
HEAD, Fleet - Street, LONDON.

Science. It was a pegging out of a claim which has been made effective. The Society after a life—as with all such societies—of fluctuating periods of greater and lesser activity, flourishes still, and its library and herbarium, transferred to the Crown when space demand of their bulk became urgent, have been the foundation for the large botanical library and herbarium now maintained and subsidised by Government in the Royal Botanic Garden.[7]

Hutton Balfour himself donated several books to the Society's Library. He was also instrumental in adding to that Library, the botanical libraries of the Plinian Society of Edinburgh and of the Wernerian Natural History Society. (See pp. 51–52). Ultimately, in 1872, as Regius Keeper of the Garden, he received the Library of the Society and provided suitable accommodation for it with financial help from the Government. He persuaded James McNab, the Curator of the Garden, to look after the Library until 1876 when he succeeded in obtaining Government authority to appoint a Curator of the Herbarium who would also supervise the Library. (See p. 57).

The Library today has scores of books bearing the bookplates of Hutton Balfour (Figs 15, 16). These are from his personal library which, not only prior to, but also after the arrival of the Library of the Botanical Society at the Garden, was available to anyone who wished to use it. Shortage of space caused many of his books and those belonging to the Garden and the University to be filed together. The more valuable of his books were removed

15. John Hutton Balfour's name plate. 4×7 cm.

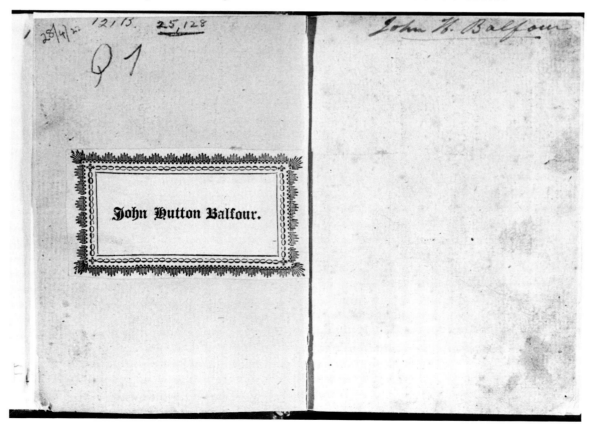

from the Garden when he retired in 1879. They were kept by his son Isaac Bayley Balfour who was to become the Regius Keeper and Professor of Botany in 1888. After Bayley Balfour's death in 1922, his library, including his father Hutton Balfour's books and papers, was given to the Garden by Lady Agnes, Bayley Balfour's widow.

THE BOTANICAL SOCIETY OF EDINBURGH AND ITS LIBRARY: 1836–1872[8]

From about the close of the eighteenth century, Edinburgh, like the rest of the country, saw the beginnings of various societies bringing together people of similar interests. Soon such societies sprung up everywhere. Most of them were active for only a short period, often leaving behind only a name. By the 1830s there were a number of societies in Edinburgh devoted to antiquarian interests, the sciences, medicine, religion, arts and crafts, law and others.[9] Of those, many of the natural history and medical societies were in one way or other connected with the University, and based there.[10] It was strange that among all those there was not one wholly concerned with botany, a subject for which Edinburgh was so well known. Efforts had been made earlier by people such as Robert Graham, the then Regius Keeper of the Royal Botanic Garden and Professor of Botany at the University, but without success.[11] However, on 8 February 1836 John Hutton Balfour, who was destined to succeed his master Graham at the Garden and at the University, called a meeting of interested friends to consider the desirability of forming a society for the study and advancement of botany. The meeting unanimously agreed to the institution of the Botanical Society of Edinburgh and set about the work with great professionalism and boundless enthusiasm. The first formal meeting was held on 17 March 1836.

Among the objectives of the Society was 'the formation in Edinburgh of an Herbarium of Foreign and British Plants and of a Library and Museum for

16. John Hutton Balfour's book plate.
10.5×6.5 cm.

OMNE SOLUM FORTI PATRIA

general consultation and reference'. The bye-laws and regulations of the Society re-stated 'the Society shall also have in view the formation of a Botanical Library and Museum, by means of donation and purchase'. One of the fundamental laws of the Society was that 'the Curator shall have charge of the Society's specimens, Museum and Library, and with the assistance of the Museum and Library Committee, shall arrange, classify, and keep a Catalogue or other account of the same'. It was stipulated that 'No purchase of books or Specimens for the Society's Library or Museum exceeding Two Pounds in value shall be made until the same shall have been approved of at an ordinary meeting' and that 'the British Secretary shall keep lists of . . . all Books, Specimens, &c., presented to or purchased by the Society . . .'[12]

The first elected President of the Society was Professor Robert Graham; Robert Kaye Greville and John Hutton Balfour were vice-presidents; Patrick Neill, Martin Barry, David Falconer, Giles Munby and Nicholas Tyacke were Councillors; William Hunter Campbell was Secretary; Edward Forbes, Foreign Secretary; William Brand, Treasurer and James McNab, Curator. Edward Forbes, Giles Munby and Nicholas Tyacke were the members of the first Museum and Library Committee.[13]

The news of the foundation of the Botanical Society of Edinburgh spread fast and messages of congratulations and promises of support came from all over the country and beyond. It was not long before the Society established links with many foreign countries. This was particularly true of the far flung outposts of the British Empire where many a Briton, whilst officially engaged in one way or another in the defence of the Empire or the administration of its various departments of Government, was, nevertheless, assiduously pursuing the study of local flora. To these, the Botanical Society of Edinburgh came as a welcome botanical link with the Mother country, because, at that time there was no other solely botanical society in Britain geared to the exchange of botanical specimens and information at an international level.

The enthusiasm and industry of the local members spurred on by the support and contributions of members and friends elsewhere in Britain and overseas resulted in the fledgling Society's remarkable growth and development. Its original membership of 21 had risen to some 450 by the time Graham died in 1845 and by the end of 1872 it was in excess of 500, and the Society was corresponding and exchanging materials with 44 other societies. Among the membership was a very sizeable number of overseas contacts, not only in Europe, but much farther afield.

The Society's Herbarium began with the contribution, on 14 April 1836, of 300 specimens of Swiss plants from Martin Barry. Thousands of specimens followed from various members. The Herbarium grew so large that it was first joined with the University Herbarium and eventually moved to the Royal Botanic Garden in 1863 to become the Garden Herbarium.

The Library of the Botanical Society of Edinburgh started with a donation from the veteran botanist and writer in Newcastle, Nathaniel John Winch on 9 June 1836. The donation consisted of two of Winch's own published works:

(1) *An essay on the geographical distribution of plants through the counties of Northumberland, Cumberland and Durham . . . second edition*, Newcastle, 1825;

(2) *Contributions to the flora of Cumberland, to which are added remarks on*

the lists of plants, published in Hutchinson's history of that county, and in Turner and Dillwyn's Botanist's Guide through England and Wales, Newcastle, printed by T & J Hodgson, 1833.

By the end of 1836 only three items had been gifted to the Library. At the close of 1837 it had 35 items. The following years saw a quickening flow of books into the Library. The list of donors became almost a complete list of botanists of the day, British and foreign. Their gifts were not only copies of some of their own published works, but of other people's works, too.[14]

One of the larger single gifts of books received by the Society in 1838 was from William Christy of Clapham Road, Stockwell. 'He was a scientific botanist, and had a considerable botanical library and herbarium, which foreseeing his early death from the nature of his disease, he presented to the Botanical Society of Edinburgh . . .'[15] The library contained 'upwards of 60 different works, many of them of great rarity and value'.[16, 17]

A similar number of books came to the Society in 1841 from the Plinian Society of Edinburgh. Instituted in 1823 for the advancement of the study of natural history, antiquities and the physical sciences in general, that Society was active until 1835. No meetings were held from then until 1841 when a special meeting, convened on 6 February, decided to wind up the Society. A motion was proposed to that effect, with the provision that the Hunterian Medical Society receive an equal share with the Royal Medical Society of the medical books of the Society. An amendment was moved that the Society should not divide its effects, but should either sell them all and found a prize, or give them all to one Society in order that the principle of commensuration be maintained. The amendment was defeated and the original motion was carried. A subcommittee consisting of A D Maclagan, J H Balfour and Robert Spittal was appointed to carry out the objects of the motion.[18]

The minutes of the Royal Medical Society recorded the receipt of the Plinian books. A large part of their library, and with it most of their Plinian books, was auctioned by Sotheby's in 1969.[19] They still have in their possession one MS entitled *A tale of the sun's rising, setting, length of day and night, planetary hour by day and night, with the sun's declination*, which belonged to the Plinian Society.

The Botanical Society received the following letter from the Plinian Society:

> At a recent meeting of the Plinian Society, a resolution was passed to the effect that the Society should be dissolved, and that the Library and Museum should be disposed of, in such a way as to promote, as far as possible, the original object of the Institution.
>
> As members of a committee appointed to carry this resolution into effect, we accordingly hereby transmit to the Botanical Society the Herbarium of the late Plinian Society, and the Books, a list of which accompanies this letter.[20]

The sub-committee had instructions only with regard to the disposal of the medical books; they were free to decide on the rest. Their decision to send the books to the Botanical Society of Edinburgh was almost predictable because it was one of the most active societies in Edinburgh at the time and Balfour and Maclagan were active members of it. Spittall, although not a member, had a keen interest in botany. At least seven of the papers and exhibitions he presented at the meetings of the Plinian Society were of botanical interest. Indeed, his paper on the diseases of plants presented on 16 December 1828 obtained the gold medal awarded by Professor Graham.[21] With such preponderance of botanical interest among the sub-committee the Plinian books at their disposal had to go to the Botanical Society.[22]

Another society whose botanical library went to the Botanical Society was the Wernerian Natural History Society of Edinburgh. Formed in 1808, by the 1840s after some years of great activity the Society had all but ceased to function. In 1856 a meeting of its members was called to consider the Society's future. One of the proposals pursued with some enthusiasm was a union of the Wernerian, Royal Physical and Botanical societies. What the effect of such a merger would have been is open to speculation. However, it did not happen. The Wernerian, therefore, decided to wind up its affairs. At a meeting on 28 November 1857 the Society decided, among other things, that two-thirds of its funds should be given to the Royal Physical Society and one-third to the Botanical Society; that all books on botanical subjects be given to the Botanical Society; all other books except such as might be required for completing the works in the College Library be handed over to the Royal Physical Society and that the furniture of the Society be handed over to the Botanical Society. In return the recipient societies were to accept the Wernerian members as their members. The two societies agreed.

However, on 23 January 1858, at the final meeting of the Wernerian Society called to approve the proposal, there was one dissident vote, that of George Macdonald, who protested against any of the funds or effects of the Wernerian being given to the Botanical Society, and threatened legal action.

Perhaps Macdonald had reason to be displeased with the botanical world, because a work entitled *The Botanist's Word-book* published by Reeves & Co., to which Macdonald's name was attached, had received very strong adverse criticism.[23] Nevertheless, the Wernerian altered the terms of the transfer so that in the event of Macdonald bringing an action, they were to be protected by each of the societies, the Royal Physical and Botanical, up to the value of the property each received from the Wernerian.[24]

Depending entirely on donations, the progress of the Society's Library was slow in the first year. It was thought that some necessary books ought to be bought when funds became available. On 12 January 1837 when the Library had only three books, David Steuart gave £5. to the Society's library fund. This was followed on 8 June of the same year by the Society placing £10. at the disposal of the library committee. It was not until 1838 that the minutes of the Society recorded purchases for its Library. The first purchase was Augustin Pyramus de Candolle, *Prodromus Systematis naturalis Regni Vegetabilis*, pars. I-VI et pars. VI (sectio prior) (1824–38), followed by: William Jackson Hooker, *British Flora*, third edition, vol. 1 (1835); John Lindley, *Synopsis of the British Flora* (1835); Carl Linné, *Système des plantes*, traduit par M J P Mouton-Fontenille, 5 tomes (1804–1805); Carl Ludwig Willdenow, *Species Plantarum* 10 tom. (1797–1810); and *Magazine of Natural History*, nos. 1–8 (1838).

Library purchases though not great in number were nevertheless a regular feature of the Society's activities for some years. Particular care seems to have been taken to acquire complete runs of some journals. All numbers of *Magazine of Natural History*, William Curtis' *Botanical Magazine*, and *Magazine of Zoology and Botany* were purchased. After 1846 no record of library purchases is seen in the Society's minutes.

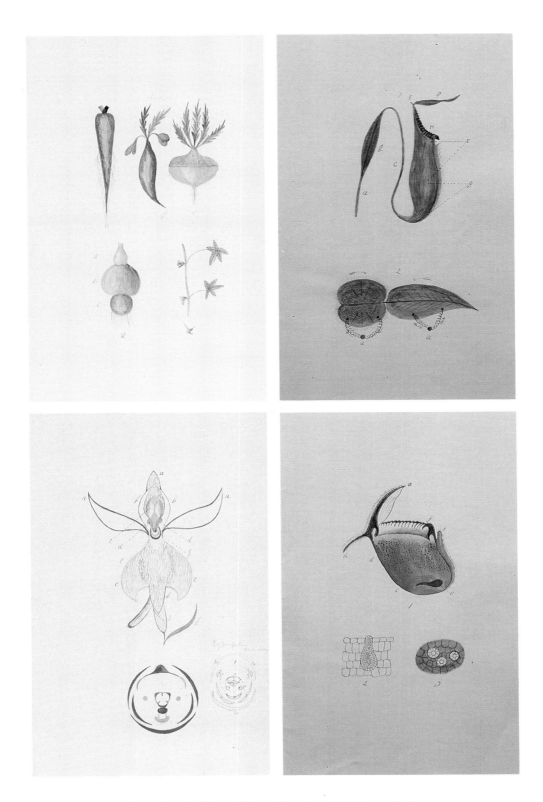

Plate 1. Examples of Alexander Dickson's illustrations used for his lectures. 20×13 cm.

Plate 2. One of the monochrome plates and its corresponding coloured plate from Pierre Joseph Redouté's Les Liliacées *in the Library. 52.5×36 cm.*

Donations and purchases were not the only sources for the growth of the Library. The Society's Annual Reports and Proceedings published regularly from the beginning, and the Transactions published from 1844 onwards brought in a large number of similar publications as exchange from many British and foreign societies and institutions. By far the larger part of the Library's periodical literature collection was obtained through this exchange of publications.

Apart from books and journals the Library also came to possess a large collection of manuscript materials. The bulk of this was the vast correspondence the Society received from all parts of the world. But the Society was also recipient of other materials including the donation of valuable manuscript papers on botanical subjects by Professor Graham received from his widow in 1846.

The Library of the Botanical Society of Edinburgh thus grew in size and importance mainly through donations and exchanges and to a lesser extent by purchases. By 1872 there were some 1,000 volumes which were more than the Society's rooms at 5 St Andrew Square could accommodate or its finances maintain in good order. The Society, therefore, decided to offer the Library to the Government. The Chairman of the library committee, William Craig, wrote to Professor J H Balfour, the then Regius Keeper of the Garden, on 23 April 1872:

> Sir, We are authorised by the Botanical Society of Edinburgh to offer, through you, the Library of the Society to H.M. Board of Works, for the purpose of forming a nucleus of a consulting library for the Herbarium in the Royal Botanic Garden of Edinburgh.
>
> The Library consists of about 1,000 volumes, and many of the books are valuable and useful for Herbarium work. You are aware that the Herbarium at the Garden is open to the public, as well as to the members of the Society, and many of them consult it. There has, however, been long felt want of books to consult in the examination of plants.
>
> The Society are aware that you, as Regius Keeper of the Garden, have endeavoured to remedy this defect by granting visitors the use of books from your own private library.
>
> The Society believe that no public collection of dried specimens of plants can be available for scientific purposes without a consulting library.
>
> They therefore wish for the sake of the public, and for the advancement of Botanical Science, to do what they can to supply the difficiency.
>
> The Society will hand over to the Government the entire Library, and continue to send any botanical works which they may from time to time receive, on the understanding that the Government will provide for their accommodation and keeping, and that they will be open for consultation to the members of the Botanical Society, as well as to the public who may wish to consult the Herbarium.
>
> The Society have desired us to send this communication to you, with the request that you will forward it to headquarters, with such statement as you may think necessary to make. The Society believe that by this offer they are conferring a great favour on the public—that they are enhancing the value of the Herbarium at the Garden—as well as

contributing in no small degree to the promotion of Botanical Science, and are thus endeavouring to secure for Scotland what England already possesses in the valuable Government Library at Kew . . .[25]

Professor Balfour forwarded the Society's letter to Mr Ayrton of HM Treasury, with a covering letter dated 16 May 1872, which said:

> Dear Sir, as Regius Keeper of the Edinburgh Botanic Garden, I have received the enclosed letter from the Botanical Society of Edinburgh, and in conformity with the request contained in it, I now forward it to you by the Hon. Commissioners of H.M. Works. At the same time I take the liberty of urging strongly the propriety of accepting the generous offer of the Society. I have long been asking for means of providing a consulting library in connection with the Herbarium in the Garden, and it is with great pleasure that I now transmit the Society's offer.
>
> The Library contains many valuable books, which will be most serviceable to those who consult the Herbarium. I have long felt that the usefulness of the collection was much impaired by the want of books.
>
> I hope, therefore, that I shall be authorised to receive the gifts on the part of the Government, and that I may ask a letter to allow uniting the books in the Herbarium Rooms.
>
> I am satisfied as to the value of the Library, and I venture in the strongest manner to suggest to you the propriety of accepting it.[26]

17. The Old Herbarium. The extension on the left was built in 1872 to accommodate the library of the Botanical Society of Edinburgh.

Mr Ayrton thought it 'very desirable to carry through the proposal'[27] and urged the Lords Commissioners of HM Treasury to sanction the expenditure necessary to build a room adjoining the Herbarium at the Garden (Fig. 17) and supply cases and shelving to accommodate the books. Mr Robert Matheson of HM Office of Works in Edinburgh wrote to Professor Balfour on 30 September

1872 that he had been directed to proceed with the work.[28] On 10 December 1872 Balfour had occasion to write to the Office of Works 'The library building will, I have no doubt, be completed before the end of March 1873 as the roof is now nearly finished and a considerable part of the shelving is ready'.[29]

Thus was the library of the Botanical Society of Edinburgh handed over to the Royal Botanic Garden in Edinburgh.

THE GARDEN LIBRARY: 1872–1887[30]

Library provision at the Garden, as we have seen, was far from adequate for the purpose of the Garden, its Herbarium and the over 300 students who attended lectures there. The Botanical Society on the other hand had a fast growing library which, rather than in isolation at the Society's rooms, would be more useful at the Garden in the Herbarium where the members of the Society carried on their botanical investigations.

These matters must long have been the topics of conversation and discussion at the Garden, at the Society and between the Garden staff and the public who used the Garden and the Herbarium, most of whom were members of the Society. Out of this was born first the idea and then the proposal to present the Library to the Garden through the Government. The Society could have gifted their Library directly to the Garden. But to provide suitable accommodation to house it the Garden would have had to seek Government financial help. Such help would be more easily obtained if Government received something valuable in return for the money they were asked to spend. Possibly the men at the Garden and the Society also believed that such a valuable gift as the Library would prompt the Government to support the Library financially. But it was not to be. The Government were happy to receive a large collection of books and provide the necessary accommodation for it. In fact, this was all they were asked to do and this was all they were prepared to do. Further hopeful appeals for financial help for the Library received the same negative reply of earlier years.

One ought to remember that in 1872–73 when these events were taking place, the Garden was not a Government establishment. It received grants from Government, and was obliged to submit accounts for that money. However, the Government had no real control over the Garden and its finances. Its responsibility to see to the needs of the Garden was, if anything, limited. It is, therefore, not surprising that the Government was not forthcoming with financial commitments over which it had no effective control. This view is strengthened by the fact that when the Garden became a total Government responsibility some money was made available specifically for the Library's needs.

The arrival of the collection from the Botanical Society was a great boost to the Library at the Garden. Yet, valuable as it was, the Library still lacked many books necessary for the work of the Garden, and more particularly for the taxonomic work in the Herbarium. The Regius Keeper in his annual reports named some of these books more than once.

There are still many important works required by those who prosecute their studies in the Herbarium Room; among these may be noticed De

Candolle's *Prodromus*, of which we have only a few early volumes, Hooker and Bentham's *Genera Plantarum*, Kunth's *Enumeratio Plantarum*, Pritzell's *Thesaurus*, Pfeiffer's *Nomenclator Botanicus*, Hooker and Baker's *Synopsis Filicum*, Schimper's *Musci Europaei*, Agardh's *Algae*, Cooke's works *On Fungi*, Crombie's *Lichens*, the Floras of various countries, some of which are published at the expense of Government, and ought to be in the Library of the Royal Garden . . .[31]

The enhancement of the Library was very much on the Regius Keeper's mind. His own personal financial situation did not allow him to add all that he wanted to the Library. Nevertheless, he placed in the Library copies of all his own published works and others he could afford. Donations from the Botanical Society kept coming in. Sixty items were sent by the Royal Academy of Sciences in Stockholm, including: Nils Johan Andersson, *Monographia Salicum*, I (1867); Oswald Heer, *Die Miocene Flora und Fauna Spitzergens* (1870); and Veit Brecher Wittrock, *Försök till en Monographi öfver algslägtet Monostroma* (1866). A similar number of very valuable botanical works was received from Dr Robert Dickson, a close friend and admirer of Hutton Balfour. Graduating MD from Edinburgh in 1826, he practiced medicine in London for many years, at the same time lecturing on Botany at the medical school in Webb Street and later at St George's Hospital. His donations included the first 14 volumes of De Candolle's *Prodromus*, the later volumes of which work Hutton Balfour had specifically mentioned as lacking in the Library. It also contained: Gottlieb Wilhelm Bischoff, *Der Botanik* (1834–1840) 3 vols.; Jean Baptise Francois Bulliard, *Herbier de la France*,

18. Title pages of John Dalton's Hortus Siccus. 32×21 cm. (see Appendix X— DALTON, John)

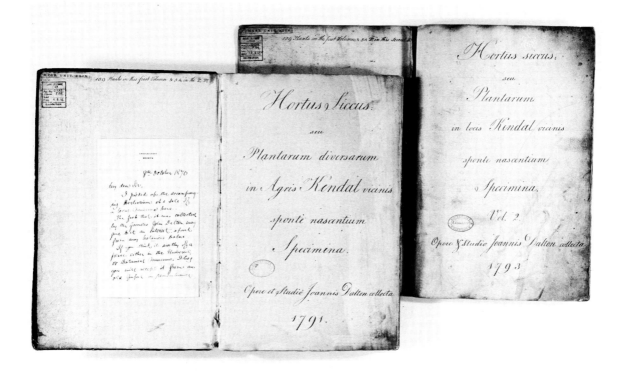

(1784–1791) 8 vols.; and Achille Richard, *Monographie de la Famille des Élaeagnées* (1824). Old friends like Delpino, Morren, Babington and many others also continued to send their donations to the Library. The number of monographs received was, however, not satisfactory, and the great number of separates and reprints of papers and more particularly of society publications from various places was beginning to crowd the shelves. Hutton Balfour was still concerned with the lack of quality of the stock especially for taxonomic work in the Herbarium. So it was that on 30 September 1876 he launched a special appeal on behalf of

THE LIBRARY IN THE ROYAL BOTANIC GARDEN OF EDINBURGH. The Botanical Society of Edinburgh having presented their collection of Books to the Government, these, with additions since received, are now arranged in a room connected with the Herbarium at the Royal Botanic Garden, and the library thus constituted is under the superintendence of Mr Webb, Curator of the Herbarium.

To the Botanical Students and others who visit the Garden and consult the Herbarium, this Government Library is available daily from 10 am to 5 pm, and as Regius Keeper of the Garden, I am very anxious to obtain such accessions as will render it more useful for their service. During the years 1874, 1875, and 1876, the number of Students annually attending the Lectures in the Garden has amounted to nearly 350, and many of them devote part of their time to the study of plants in the Garden and in the Herbarium. These Students and others who are prosecuting researches in Botany necessarily require the use of a good library. In connection with the Herbarium itself, it is further necessary for ready reference in the determination of plants and specimens transmitted to the Garden and the Herbarium, that the Library should contain a series of standard Systematic Works, Monographs, Foreign and Colonial Floras, etc. Of such a collection the nucleus exists, but much more is still required.

Many of my Botanical Friends have already kindly made valuable donations, and I doubt not will continue to render assistance, both directly and by communicating to others our wants and circumstances. I am indebted to certain Learned Societies for their Proceedings and Transactions. I am anxious to induce Societies at home and abroad to issue botanical papers, to contribute copies of their publications; and I trust that former pupils of the Edinburgh School will continue to add to the Library such works as will be serviceable to their successors.

Government does not make ANY allowance for the purchase of books, and there is no fund available for the purpose from any other sources.

To the printed Annual Report of the Garden is appended a list of Donations to the Library, with the names of the Donors.

It is desirable that each work should bear the inscription—"For the Library, Royal Botanic Garden, from . . ."

Contributions will be thankfully received and duly acknowledged by me . . .[32]

Hutton Balfour's appeal merits close examination. Taken at its face value, it may be interpreted to mean that there was no library at the Garden before the books from the Botanical Society got there, although it does not say so in so many words. But we have seen that there was a collection of books at the Garden, paid for with garden funds from at least 1766 onwards. And there were books presented to the Garden Library before 1872 by well-wishers, for example, a copy of Sutherland's Catalogue of 1683, clearly inscribed as a gift to the Garden Library, in 1861. More importantly, there was Hutton Balfour's own library, which, like those of his predecessors, was part of the Garden and available to anyone for consultation.

The more interesting part of the appeal is where Balfour speaks of the lack of money for the purchase of books. That the Government did not provide any money for the purchase of books cannot be disputed; but his statement 'there is no fund available for the purpose from any other source' is in direct conflict with the statement, in the same year as the appeal, made by John Small, the then University Librarian in Edinburgh, to the Universities (Scotland) Commission. Small said: 'the botanical department (alone) would swallow up nearly the whole of our funds'.[33]

The records of the University show that the Botany Department was supplied with books from University funds.[34] The University's entire Department of Botany, its staff and students, class rooms, lectures, laboratories and other educational facilities were at the Garden. It stands to reason that their departmental class library, funded by the University, was at the Garden, too. The Essays on the history of the Edinburgh University Library do not specifically mention the botany class library.[35] However, the University had a library at the Garden at least by 1826 when Robert Graham spoke of his department library as very inadequate and lacking staff to serve the students.[3]

Also, the Edinburgh University Calendar for 1858–59 and following years clearly states: 'Rooms at the Garden are open to the pupils for the consultation of Books of Plates, Periodicals and other Botanical works . . .' The statement is absent in the calendars for 1871–72 and 1872–73, but appears again in 1873–74 and the following years as: 'There is also a library in a room adjoining the herbarium. This library has been presented by the Edinburgh Botanical Society'. The University surely did not deprive its students attending lectures at the Garden in 1871–73 of the use of books there. More likely, perhaps, the withdrawal of the statement about the Library was a calculated move by all concerned, to influence the Government to accept the offer of the Botanical Society Library for the Garden, to provide suitable accommodation for it and to help with its growth and development—a move which was not altogether unsuccessful because, the Government did provide new accommodation for the Library. (See pp. 54–55).

It would seem, therefore, that Hutton Balfour did not consider the University class library as part of the Garden establishment. His appeal was possibly also implying that the University's library at the Garden did not contain many of the necessary works on systematic botany which was as important a function at the time as the teaching of botany. The former case is understandable because although Balfour was in every sense the Professor of Botany of the University, with all the duties and rights of that position truly vested in him, that part of his responsibilities was quite distinct and separate from his position and responsibility in the Garden, and he wanted to keep it that way. Also, the University books at the Garden were the property of the University; they were, at best, on long-term loan and so liable to be removed any time, as was the Regius Keeper's own library. This was, in fact, what happened. Not long after the separation of the two posts of Regius Keeper of the Garden and the Professor of Botany at the University in 1956, the University's books, which had stood beside the Garden's books in the Garden Library for years, were removed to the University Library in 1965.[36] The main library kept expensive taxonomic works and the class library at Kings Buildings held mostly textbooks for the use of students there. Perhaps it was Balfour's intention to ensure that there was a library at the Garden which was not likely to disappear.

The suggestion that the University class library at the Garden did not contain many of the necessary standard works on systematic botany is largely, but not wholly, true. Many of the books bought by the University Library at the recommendation of the Professor of Botany were not exactly undergraduate textbooks; they were standard taxonomic works of the time. It is likely that not all of them were kept at the Garden, because only few, if any, of the University students at the Garden were concerned with taxonomic botany and therefore had only limited use for them. The people who would have wanted to use those books were mostly non-student members of the public, especially members of the Botanical Society, and hence not really a University responsibility. It needs to be stressed, however, that, certainly in the later years, some of the taxonomically important books of the University were on long-term loan to the Garden. Compte de Hippolyte Francois Jaubert and Eduardo Spach, *Illustrationes Plantarum orientalium* . . . (1842–1857) 5 vols, and John Sibthorp and James Edward Smith, *Flora Graeca* . . . (1806–1840) 10 vols are just two examples.[37]

Hutton Balfour's appeal on behalf of the Royal Botanic Garden Library was a success in that the total number of donations received was much increased. But they were largely smaller works—pamphlets, separates, reprints—or Transactions, Proceedings and Reports from botanical friends, societies or institutions in various parts of the country and abroad. Although the value of the items was high, they were not what Balfour was looking for.

One of the problems of a growing library is accommodation. The room provided by the Government could not contain the whole stock of the Library. Balfour hoped that Inverleith House in the Garden which was being renovated as the official residence for the Regius Keeper would have room enough for a library. In his reports on the matter he said:

> . . . A most important want in the house is a room for a library—specially Botanical. The building of such a room is not included in the present estimate for the repair of the house, but it is to be hoped that it will be arranged next year. The Library is of importance not only to the Regius Keeper himself, but also for the various visitors who study in the Garden. At present there is a very small room connected with the Herbarium building, which contains chiefly the Transactions of Societies, sent in exchange for those of the Botanical Society of Edinburgh, the members of which kindly handed over their Library to the Government. It contains scarcely any works of reference required by those who are studying the floras of the various parts of the world. Such visitors, therefore, are, by the permission of the Regius Keeper, allowed to avail themselves of the use of his private library.[38]

The arrangements for the accommodation of the Library have not yet been carried out and at the present the books are scattered through various rooms, rendering the consultation of them by the Regius Keeper and Garden visitors very inconvenient.[39]

It is interesting to note that the room built specifically for the reception and housing of the Botanical Society Library could hold only the Transactions of Societies. It is incredible that the Government would have built the room so small that it was insufficient to accommodate the whole of the gift it was receiving. Certainly there was no complaint from any quarter at the time of the planning and construction of the room. It is more likely that the monographs, as opposed to serials of the Botanical Society, when united with those already existing in the Garden, formed so large a collection that other accommodation had to be found for it. Such other accommodation was in the Regius Keeper's new house which was intended to have proper accommodation for a botanical library, but, in fact, did not have. When Balfour asked for room for a specially botanical library, it must have been his intention to have the Garden Library there, not just his private library, because he visualised a large and important botanical library which would be used by many. In the circumstances, Balfour had little choice but to accommodate the books, his own and the Garden's, scattered through various rooms in the already crammed rooms in the Garden and in his house at 27 Inverleith Row. This inevitably must have resulted in the mixing of the books from different sources, thus making this scattered library more nearly a Garden Library than any of the libraries of the earlier Regius Keepers. Perhaps this was why Hutton Balfour did not remove all his personal library from the Garden when he retired in 1879—it would have been too difficult to separate his books from the rest. The Library of the Garden remained scattered in different rooms for well nigh a hundred years; it was not to have its own accommodation until the present Herbarium and Library building was opened in 1964.[40]

ALEXANDER DICKSON

Alexander Dickson, who succeeded Hutton Balfour in 1880, was a conscientious, meticulous and thorough teacher. He took great pains over the preparation of his lectures and the illustrations which accompanied them. Some of his lecture notes and exquisite illustrations (Plate 1) are in the Library. So too are the many scientific papers he published in journals such as the *Transactions and Proceedings of the Royal Society of Edinburgh, Transactions and Proceedings of the Botanical Society of Edinburgh, Edinburgh New Philosophical Journal, Journal of Botany, Edinburgh Medical Journal* and *Glasgow Medical Journal.* The Library also contains his donations.

Dickson was the first Regius Keeper who succeeded in obtaining Government approval to buy books and journals from the Garden's general fund. In the first year in office he bought at least eight out of twenty-five books and five out of nine journals added to the Library, from garden funds. By 1884 the purchases were increasing in number and value. Possibly this was more than the Government had expected and so restrictions were imposed: in 1885 no purchases were made other than two journals. In the following year no money seems to have been available from garden funds. Dickson, therefore, had to step in and pay for at least two journals from his own pocket to ensure their receipt in the Library without a break.[41] How Dickson would have handled this situation further is hard to say: he died suddenly on 30 December 1887.

Dickson's purchases for the Library were marked by the official stamp which said: 'Supplied for the public Service'. It is also interesting to note that the books and journals added to the Library reflected both the taxonomic and horticultural interests in the Garden.

As Professor of Botany in the University of Edinburgh Dickson was involved in the purchase of books for the Department of Botany. The University Librarian's annual reports to the Library Committee, of which Dickson was a member, record the amount spent each year on botanical books. Some at least of these must have been deposited in the Garden for the use of the University students attending lectures there.

Dickson's own personal effects, including his library[42] and museum pieces,[43] were removed from the Garden by his brother Archibald Dickson when Alexander died in 1887 after only a relatively short period of seven years in office.

NOTES AND REFERENCES

1. FLETCHER, Harold Roy and BROWN, William Hunter (1970). *Royal Botanic Garden Edinburgh 1670–1970.* Edinburgh, HMSO, p. 102.

2. Statement by the Directors of the Royal Botanic Institution of Glasgow, read at a Special Meeting of Proprietors on Friday, 13 April, 1883, p. 3:
As early as 1818 "a scientific and popular course of lectures had been given". At this early period, too, a library was founded in the Garden, and it is worthy to note that a botanical artist was retained on the staff to sketch and paint any plants of scientific interest blooming in the Garden . . .

3. *Evidence, oral and documentary, taken and received by the Commissioners appointed by His Majesty George IV, July 23rd, 1826 and re-appointed by His Majesty William IV, October 12th 1830; for visiting the Universities of Scotland,* Vol. 1. University of Edinburgh . . . London, HMSO, 1837, p. 264.

4. *Catalogue of the valuable Botanical library and extensive herbarium of the late Robert Graham, FRS. Regius Professor of Botany in the University of Edinburgh* . . . which will be sold by Auction by Messrs C B Tait and T Nisbet in the Great Room, No. 11, Hanover Street Edinburgh, on Monday and Tuesday, April 6 and 7, 1846 at one o'clock.

5. STEINBERG, Carlo H (1977). The collectors and collections in the Herbarium Webb. *Webbia,* vol. 32, pp. 1–49. This paper deals with the various plant collections in the herbarium of the University of Florence, including Graham's, on p. 7.

6. Proceedings . . . Thursday, January 8, 1846. *Annual Reports and Proceedings of the Botanical Society of Edinburgh,* 1844–46, p. 10.

7. BALFOUR, Isaac Bayley: A sketch of the Professors of Botany in Edinburgh from 1670 until 1887. *In* OLIVER, F W (ed.) (1913) *Makers of British botany* . . . Cambridge University Press, p. 294.

8. For references in this section see also the minute books, annual reports, transactions and proceedings of the societies mentioned, under the relevant dates. Minute books of the Botanical Society of Edinburgh are in the RBG Library, Edinburgh. Records of the other societies are in the Edinburgh University Library. Published reports, transactions and proceedings will be available in larger libraries.

9. *The Edinburgh Almanack* . . . for 1830 . . . pp. 334–345, and other years and relevant pages.

10. FINALYSON, C P (1958, 1963). Records of medical and scientific societies in Scotland, II, Records of scientific and medical societies preserved in the University Library, Edinburgh. *The Bibliotheck*, vol. 1, no. 3, pp. 14–19; and vol. 4, no. 1, pp. 38–39, respectively.

11. *First annual report, Laws and Transactions of the Botanical Society of Edinburgh . . .* Session 1836-7, Edinburgh, 1837, p. 25.

12. *Ibidem* pp. 11–22.

13. Minutes of the Botanical Society of Edinburgh dated 17 March and 14 April, 1836.

14. *Transactions and Proceedings of the Botanical Society of Edinburgh* for the relevant years list all donations to the library, with the names of donors.

15. *Gardener's Magazine*, 1839, vol. 15, p. 536.

16. *Ibidem* p. 262.

17. For lists of Christy's books received by the Society *see: Second Annual Report and Proceedings of the Botanical Society of Edinburgh*, 1838, pp. 87–89 and *Fourth and Fifth Annual Reports . . .* 1841, pp. 72–73.

18. The Hunterian Medical Society, founded in 1824, ceased to function in 1869. The Society's minute book for 1841 has not been traced to ascertain whether the Plinian books were received.

19. SOTHEBY & Co. (1968). *Catalogue of an important collection of medical books comprising the property of the Royal Medical Society, Edinburgh.* Edinburgh.

20. *Fourth and Fifth Annual Reports and Proceedings of the Botanical Society.* Session 1839–40 and 1840–41. Edinburgh, 1841, pp. 48–49.

21. *Transactions of the Plinian Society.* Session 1828-9. Edinburgh, 1829, p. 5.

22. For the list of Plinian books received by the Society see *Fourth and Fifth Annual Reports and Proceedings of the Botanical Society of Edinburgh*, 1841, pp. 78–79.

23. *Gardeners' Chronicle*, 1853 no. 50 (December 10) p. 791:

> It has been our lot to examine many bad books, but we never yet saw one so thoroughly worthless as this. What pretentions "George Macdonald Esq., Fellow of the Royal Educational Institute of Scotland", or "James Allan, Ph.D., A.M., &c., Professor of Chemistry in the Royal School of Medicine and Surgery, Pine Street, Manchester", who avow themselves the authors of such a farrago of disreputable blunders, may have to acquaintance with other branches of knowledge, we cannot say; but it is clear that they are profoundly ignorant of their own ignorance of the particular science which this book pretends to illustrate. Only imagine a teacher of botany telling his students that acerose is a term applied to the leaves of the Yew, that acina (proh pudor!) is the name of the "small granules which make up a bramble or Mulberry"—as if there were the smallest analogy between these two kinds of fruit; that the arillus is "the outer cover of a seed", and that placentation is "the arrangement of cotyledons at the time the seed is beginning to grow!!!" Messrs Reeves are respectable publishers, who have a character to lose, and many of the works brought forward by them deserve all praise. We therefore trust they will see the propriety of instantly withdrawing a book which is perfectly disgraceful to all concerned in its publication, and which is only fit to be consigned the trunk-maker.

24. Events leading to the dissolution of the Wernerian Society and the disposal of its funds and other effects are recorded in the minutes of the Botanical Society of Edinburgh. But there is no mention of the books received. This was possibly due to the difficulties of the situation. However, the list of books, money and furniture sent to the Botanical Society and that Society's acknowledgement of receipt of them, are to be seen in the minute book of the Wernerian in the Edinburgh University Library.

25. Minutes of the Botanical Society of Edinburgh, dated 30 April 1872.

26. *Ibidem* dated 9 May 1872.

27. *Ibidem* dated 5 June 1872.

28. *Ibidem* dated 14 November 1872.

29. Memorandum on the Edinburgh Royal Botanic Garden in reply to Queries from HM Office of Works—dated 10 December 1872.

30. For references in this section not listed here see the *Annual Reports of the Royal Botanic Garden, Edinburgh,* and the *Transactions and Proceedings of the Botanical Society of Edinburgh,* for the relevant years.

31. Royal Botanic Garden Edinburgh, Report for the year 1876, p. 3; and repeated in the report for 1878, p. 4.

32. Copies of the original printed appeal are in the RBG Library, Edinburgh.

33. Quoted by SIMPSON, S M: History of the library, 1837–1939. *In* GUILD, Jean R and LAW, Alexander (eds) (1982). *Edinburgh University library, 1580–1980; a collection of historical essays.* Edinburgh, University Library, p. 80.

34. SHEPHERD, Christine: The inter-relationship between the library and teaching in the seventeenth and eighteenth centuries. *In* GUILD, Jean R and LAW, Alexander (eds) (1982). *Edinburgh University Library, 1580–1980: a collection of historical essays.* Edinburgh, University Library, p. 80.

35. BELL, Margaret D: Faculty and class libraries. *In* GUILD, Jean R and LAW, Alexander (eds) (1982). *Edinburgh University Library, 1580–1980: a collection of historical essays.* Edinburgh, University Library, pp. 163–181.

36. BROWN, William Hunter: Talk to the Edinburgh and East of Scotland Branch of the Scottish Library Association, 1971. (Unpublished; see Appendix VIII).

37. These books, vital for the work of the herbarium were kept in the Garden Library for some years but are now in the University Library in George Square. The Garden has acquired a microfiche copy of Jaubert and Spach; to use Sibthorp and Smith garden staff go to George Square.

38. Royal Botanic Garden Edinburgh; Report by the Regius Keeper for the year 1877, p. 1–2.

39. *Ibidem* 1878, p. 2.

40. FLETCHER, Harold Roy and BROWN, William Hunter (1970). *Royal Botanic Garden Edinburgh 1670–1970.* Edinburgh, HMSO, pp. 258–261.

41. List of additions to the library published in the *Transactions of the Botanical Society of Edinburgh* for the relevant years specify items purchased by the Garden and gifted by Dickson.

42. A letter dated 28 August 1888 from Robert Lindsay to Bayley Balfour mentions that Archibald Dickson was prepared to dispose of his brother Alexander Dickson's set of Curtis' *Botanical Magazine.* The letter is quoted in Notes and References no. 24 on pp. 89–90. Obviously Alexander Dickson's library was removed from the Garden by his brother.

43. Letter dated 23 June 1901 from Bayley Balfour to Sir William Turner, Financial Secretary to the University of Edinburgh says that Archibald Dickson claimed all organographical specimens and manufactured articles of his brother, Alexander Dickson, at the death of the latter, to hand over to Geddes. The letter is in the RBG Library, Edinburgh.

6 The Libraries at Inverleith II, 1888-1970

ISAAC BAYLEY BALFOUR

In 1888 Isaac Bayley Balfour was appointed to the posts left vacant by the death of Alexander Dickson. At the time, the state of the Garden and its management were far from satisfactory. In his opening address of the first session of the Royal Botanic Garden Mutual Improvement Association, delivered in the Lecture Hall of the Royal Botanic Garden on Tuesday, 7 November, 1899, Bayley Balfour referred to the state of the Garden at the time he took charge there. He said:

> I do not need to go back to the time when I first knew this Botanic Garden for a contrast of conditions of then and now, the beginning, barely a dozen years ago, of the period during which the direction of its affairs has been in my hands gives abundant data for a comparison. At that time the Establishment had as an educational institution and as a Scientific garden sunk from its previous high estate. So far as its staff were concerned it had come to be very much a place in which to pension off old men unable to get other work to do—I do not know what the average age of members of the staff was, but I well recollect one old man, the chief painter of plant labels, who was only about eighty and whose fitness for work may be gauged by the fact that he was practically stone-blind—and you will readily understand that to a staff such as then existed wanting the buoyancy and energy of youth a movement like that we are to-night inaugurating would be altogether an impossibility and the question of education was beyond the pale of consideration. In the matter, too, of the progressive improvement of the Garden as such and its maintenance as a centre of instruction to the public such a staff created an impasse—what could there be but stagnation! The small amount of effort available was equal to no more than the preservation of, or, rather to the staying of too conspicuous a relapse from the status quo. The whole policy of the garden had become one of aloofness from the general public the outcome of a sense of inadequacy. The best plants were not exhibited, but kept in retired and locked places to which only a few special visitors were admitted and the furnishing of information to the public regarding the plants in the collection was discouraged and refused on the principle—as it was concisely stated to me by one then in authority—'if I give the public information they'll soon be as wise as ourselves.' . . . We have in the past decade had to take successively in hand and are now still engaged with alterations required for years but which were left undone. There is yet much to do but venture to hope we shall ere many years are gone have reconstituted the Garden in a manner which will make it worthy of its old reputation.[1]

In his obituary of Bayley Balfour, Professor F O Bower, the then President of the Royal Society in London, wrote:

> Coming thus back to his native spot, Balfour again galvanised a nerveless regime into activity. But here he found a larger problem than

in Glasgow or in Oxford. The reconstruction of the Edinburgh establishment from top to bottom became the chief aim of his life, and it took him thirty-four years to accomplish it. He lived henceforth in and for the Garden, and for the University Department centred within it. He was not often seen outside its boundary, a subject of remark sometimes by those at a distance who neither knew nor understood the work or the man.

The Edinburgh Botanic Garden in 1888 was of limited dimensions: it was separated from the Arboretum by a high wall. The plant-houses were of old design and decaying: the cultivation not beyond reproach. Though the collections included many and varied specimens, they were grown awkward and "leggy", owing to the cramped conditions under which they lived. The laboratories were out of date, and the administration rooms insufficient. In fact, the whole establishment required reorganisation. Balfour came to it, not as a tornado destroying ruthlessly, but as a new climate with storms that remove what is rotten but leave standing what is fit for use . . .[2]

A great deal of planning and hard work were needed to lift the institution to its rightful position as a national centre of botanical and horticultural study and research. To this daunting task, Balfour applied himself with vision and vigour. His first concern was to settle the question of the Garden's status and the arrangement for its financing. Kew Gardens, although founded some 90 years later than the Edinburgh Garden,[3] had already been a Government responsibility for some years. Balfour wanted the same or similar arrangement for Edinburgh to ensure continuity at a reasonable level of efficiency. With characteristic zeal and skill he put forward his arguments in support of his case (Appendix III). He did not have to wait long for the success of his campaign: the Universities (Scotland) Act of 1889[4] conferred the responsibility for the Edinburgh Garden on the Commissioners of HM Works and Public Buildings, who at the time were responsible also for the Kew Gardens.[5] This was a very important development which played a significant part in the progress the Garden was to make in the years that followed.

Despite the weighty and complex matters that engaged Balfour's attention, the Library was among his high priorities throughout his period in office and even after his retirement. Before he came to Edinburgh, as Sherardian Professor of Botany at Oxford, he 'thoroughly reorganised the valuable herbarium and library as to make them both better available for study'.[6] Dissemination of information was important to him, and for this reason he took the lead in founding the journal *Annals of Botany*, in 1887, and accepted its first editorship.[6] This journal today enjoys wide circulation and reputation. In January 1900, within twelve years of his taking charge in Edinburgh, he published the first issue of the *Notes from the Royal Botanic Garden, Edinburgh*, which from its humble beginnings has grown into one of the more important international journals devoted mainly to the publication of research papers on taxonomic botany.

Almost immediately after the Government assumed responsibility for the Garden Balfour asked for, and got, an allowance for the Library,[7] which all his predecessors had failed to do. Besides his own ability to present his case, he had the support of many men of position and influence. Among them was his counterpart at Kew, Sir William Turner Thiselton-Dyer, himself a staunch believer in the indispensability of a good library to carry out the work of a botanical garden. Thiselton-Dyer's letter to the Government dated 28 October 1888 is ample evidence for his concern for the Library under his charge at Kew (Appendix IV). Not surprisingly, he understood Balfour's anxiety for the Library at Edinburgh, and was ready to help by putting in a word of persuasion at the right time to the right people. He, in fact, was instrumental in persuading the Government to allocate £30. for the purchase of books for the Edinburgh Library.[8] He also sent to the Edinburgh Library several hundred books withdrawn from the Kew Library[9] and some more from the library of the notable botanist George Bentham which was placed at his disposal.[10]

Balfour was pleased that the Government accepted in principle that money should be allocated specifically for library purchases. He would have liked more than the £30. provided, and said so in as many words to the Committee appointed in 1890 to inquire 'into the position of the Regius Keeper of the Botanic Garden, Edinburgh, and as to the scale on which the outlay on that establishment is to be calculated for the future'. The Committee referred to this in their report of December 1890:

> Dr Bayley Balfour has represented to us very strongly that the amount now allowed for the purchase of books is inadequate. But as the allowance has only recently been fixed by your Lordships, we have not felt at liberty to seek to reopen this question—the more so, as the library has just received an important addition from the Ball Trustees. It may, however, in course of time become desirable to reconsider the amount of the allowance.[11]

'An important addition from the Ball Trustees' referred to in the report was the large number of books from the library of John Ball (Fig. 19), the alpine traveller and botanist, who died in 1889. He was a friend and correspondent of Bayley Balfour's father John Hutton Balfour, and had strong connections with Kew, and the Royal Society of London of which he was a Fellow. A man of private means, he had a very considerable botanical library and herbarium both of which he wanted to be given for the 'sole object of promoting the knowledge of natural science'.[12, 13] J D Hooker of Kew and G G Stokes of the

19. John Ball's book plate: 11 × 6.5 cm.

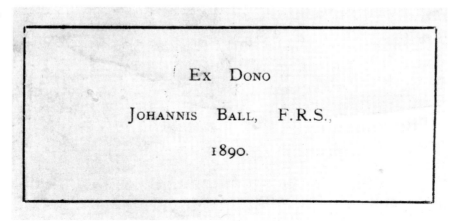

Ex Dono

Johannis Ball, F.R.S.,

1890.

Royal Society of London were to see that Ball's wishes with regard to his herbarium and library were honoured. Both of them knew and respected Balfour and his needs, and there was no doubt about the propriety of the Edinburgh Library getting the books from the Ball collection. Kew, of course, had the first choice of the books. Even then, Edinburgh obtained a very valuable collection which it would hardly have had a chance to acquire otherwise.[14]

It took the Government some four years to reconsider the amount of library allowance. In 1894 it was raised from £30. to £100.[15] This was still far from adequate for the level of library purchases Balfour had in mind. Undaunted, he restated his case and within two months the Treasury gave fresh instructions for the financial administration of the Library.[16] It would seem from some of the correspondence of the time that the Treasury kept the library allowance at the original £30., but for any exceptional purchase in Edinburgh in excess of that amount, application was to be made to the Controller of the Stationery Office. Balfour was happier with this arrangement than with the £100. offered earlier. Through the Stationery Office he bought some 'good books' certainly costing more than £100.[17] Balfour was, however, far from satisfied and repeatedly asked for more money. He had some very influential people in high positions to support him, such as R C Munro Ferguson, MP, Spring Rice of the Treasury and others. Munro Ferguson raised the matter in the House of Commons in 1897,[18] and in the following year, according to Balfour, the matter was clinched.[19] No records of the actual amount placed at Balfour's disposal for library purchases have yet been traced. Some of the letters of the time that are available, however, suggest that although Balfour might have obtained some more money, it fell short of his needs, and for years he was striving to get the means with which to enhance the resources of the Library. At the time of his retirement in 1922 he was pressing the Treasury for more funds for the Library. He wanted his successor at the Garden, William Wright Smith, to continue the effort, offering him help and guidance as to how to proceed.[19]

The gift of the collection of very valuable books from Kew and from the library of John Ball must have strengthened Balfour's ambition and enthusiasm for the Library at the Garden. He spent considerable time compiling a list of the books he wanted in the Library. His own personal knowledge of the extent of botanical literature at the time, his acquaintance of the content of the botanical library at Oxford and his association with the leading publishers and booksellers, must have helped him in this. By 1895 he had a list of almost 1,500 titles, with their prices, totalling some £4,500.[20] Acquiring these books was a principal task he set for himself.

Needless to say, this was a very difficult undertaking. Balfour could not have even hoped to be given the kind of money he was seeking. Even if he had been given it, it would not have been possible for him to obtain every title without delay, because many of them were old and scarce and came to the second-hand book market only rarely. The process of acquiring the books, therefore, had to be a gradual one, spread over several years.

Government money at his disposal for book purchase, as we have seen, was limited. In practice, however, Treasury did not stick strictly to the allowance of £30. Also, when special occasions arose, like some rare expensive books required in the Library becoming available for purchase, they were to be acquired through the Stationery Office without becoming a charge on the Garden's vote. In May 1898 Balfour was allowed to purchase books worth no less than £113., as a special case.[21]

Balfour put to good use the provision for the purchase of books through the Stationery Office. Only a couple of weeks prior to his acquiring a 'good' collection of books through the special permission of the Treasury, he had sent in a request for the purchase, through the Controller of the Stationery Office, of books costing over £100., and Balfour was optimistic of the outcome.[17]

These are not isolated instances of the Treasury and the Stationery Office coming to Balfour's assistance. There are in the Library, several invoices and receipts for books bought during the years 1896 to 1907. Among them are two from Dulau & Co. of London, one dated December 1896 for £53. 3s. 8d. and the other dated April 1899 for £40. 15s. 9d., and one from James Thin, Edinburgh dated 1902 for £40. 4s. 6d. These amounts are clearly in excess of the £30. limit of the library allowance and Balfour could not have settled them without recourse to the arrangements he had with the Treasury and the Stationery Office.

Balfour also had access to some funds from the University of Edinburgh. The University was obliged to contribute towards the upkeep of its Herbarium housed at the Garden. The money thus received was at Balfour's disposal and he used part of it to buy books. Among the invoices and receipts mentioned earlier are some for the years 1896 to 1905, which clearly show that the amounts are to be 'charged to the University Herbarium Account'. The amounts are not large, except, perhaps, the £12. 12s. 0d. to James Thin of Edinburgh in 1896, and £34. 16s. 0d. and £15. 4s. 8d. to Dulau & Co. of London, in 1903 and 1905, respectively.

Another source from which Balfour procured books was the University Library. The University Librarian's annual report to his Committee from even the time of John Hutton Balfour onwards show the amount of money spent on books for the various departments every year. At least some of these books, particularly suitable for undergraduate study, must have been sent to the Library at the Garden where all staff and students of the University Department of Botany had their classes and laboratories. The Library at the Garden has several books on its shelves which are clearly marked with a sticker which says 'University Grant'. This suggests that at some time the University gave a special grant for purchase of books for the Garden Library.

Balfour was not satisfied by the number of books he could buy with Government money and University funds. He must have felt particularly unhappy when lack of public funds prevented him from acquiring valuable second-hand books which came onto the market at sales or auctions. So, very early in his career at the Garden he began to buy books for himself. He was especially fascinated by the provenance of books, the more so if they had once belonged to someone connected with the Garden. How he bought the copy of the 1485(?) *Latin Herbarius* in 1900 has already been mentioned. (See pp. 29, 33). The greater reason for its purchase was, probably, that it once belonged to James Sutherland, the first Regius Keeper of the Garden and hence Balfour's predecessor. Even before that, in 1890, he bought the original edition of Sowerby's *English Botany*. The note relating to its purchase says: 'Sowerby's English Botany. Original Edition. Copy belonged to Prof. Graham. Catalogue price £18 8s. Paid £12 12s. January, 1890'. Many of the books Balfour bought

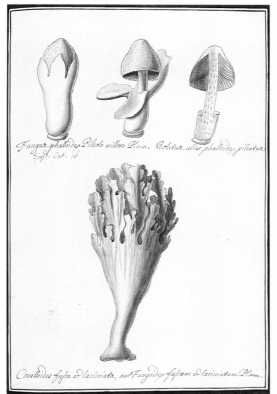

Fungus phalloides Pileolo villoso Plum. *Boletus alius phalloides pileatus.*
fig. Cat. 16.

Coralloides fusca & laciniata, aut Fungoides fuscum & laciniatum Plum.

Fungus mediæ magnitudinis, pileolo superne è rufo flavicante, lamellis
subtus sordide virentibus. Raj. Synops. 12.

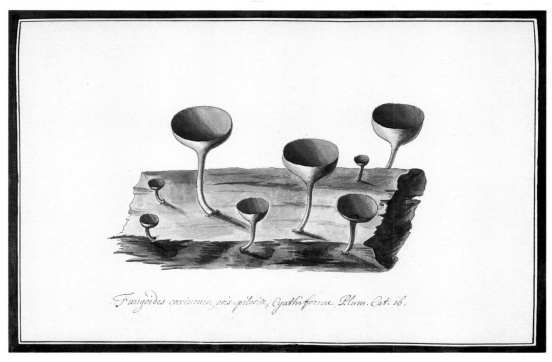

Fungoides coccineum, oris pilosis, Cyathiforme Plum. Cat. 16.

Plate 3. *Examples of drawings in Aubriet & Vaillant's* Champignons et Plantes Fongueuses. *45×31 cm.*

Plate 4. Title page and some of the plates in Anna Atkins' Cyanotype photographs of British Algae. 26×21 cm.

for himself were left at the Garden Library when he retired in 1922, or were sent there from his retirement or after his death. Second copies of those of his books which were already in the Garden were sent to other libraries such as the Bodleian in Oxford.

Some of the books he bought were for use by official or unofficial plant collectors in other parts of the world. He bought two sets of Hooker's *Flora of British India*, 7 vols, one in 1903 and the other in 1905, at £12. a set. The 1903 set was sent to Colonel Wahab, attached to the Aden Hinterland and Boundary Commission, and the 1905 set was sent to George Forrest, the prodigious plant collector, who was at the time in Rangoon.[22] The latter set came to the Garden in 1980 along with a collection of other Forrest material, from Forrest's son in London.

Perhaps Balfour's greatest success in augmenting the Library was through exchange of publications. This is certainly true of periodicals and serials. The Garden itself did not have any publications of its own to send out as exchanges. But one of the conditions of the transfer of the Library of the Botanical Society of Edinburgh to the Garden in 1872 was that the Society would pass on to the Garden any publication it received as donation or, more importantly, as exchange for its own publications. At the time Bayley Balfour came to the Garden, accessions in the Library via the Society were numerous. Considering that many of them were from overseas, those accessions were very valuable. Balfour believed that the Society's publications could be improved to facilitate speedier publication of research papers, and at the same time attract more and better publications in exchange for the Library. He therefore wrote to the Society on 27 December 1890, explaining his proposals at length (Appendix V).

The action Balfour wanted the Society to take was to publish its Proceedings monthly instead of at the end of each session. Referring to the suggestion that the Garden itself should issue a bulletin of its own activities he said that it would run the risk of separating the Garden from the Society which would be detrimental to the interests of both Garden and Society. The Society agreed to Balfour's proposals with the amendment that the Society should publish its Proceedings and Transactions monthly 'or at as short intervals as may be found convenient during the session'.[23]

Balfour took an active interest in the publications of the Society and in establishing fresh exchange agreements. At the end of 1890 the Society, and from it the Garden, received 97 journals and serials from 69 cities, 15 of them British. By the end of 1900, the figures were 140 titles, from 98 cities, 16 of them British. Many of these agreements, some dating back to the Society's earliest days, were still operating in 1984, and the number of publications received in the Library through this formed a substantial part of its intake of periodical publications.

By 1900 Balfour seems to have changed his mind about the Garden itself issuing an occasional publication to report its own activities. Perhaps the Society was no longer able to guarantee quick publication of research papers presented to it. Thus was born in January 1900 *Notes from the Royal Botanic Garden, Edinburgh*. The prefatory note in the first number clearly stated 'The *Notes* will be available in exchange for publications of kindred institutions . . .' Thus Balfour added strength to his programme of exchange by providing another title which could be sent out.

Gifts and bequests have been yet another means by which Balfour enhanced the value of the Library. As during the periods of his predecessors, during Bayley Balfour's time, too, several hundreds of books and journals were presented to the Library by a large number of friends, both British and foreign. Many were rare and very valuable works. One particular donation in 1888 merits special mention: the gift of one complete set of Curtis's *Botanical Magazine*, vols 1–114 (1787–1888), from Charles Jenner, Draper in Edinburgh and an active member of the Botanical Society of Edinburgh. As part of the gift, arrangements were made for the supply to the Garden of all volumes of the Magazine to be published to the end of 1898. Apart from the botanical and considerable monetary value of the gift today, it is interesting because some of the letters on this gift suggest that the set of 114 volumes presented in 1888 was probably from the library of Alexander Dickson, Balfour's immediate predecessor in office.[24] Affixed to all volumes are Jenner's own bookplates. What is even more interesting is that the earlier volumes also have the bookplates of J C Loudon, the well-known botanical and horticultural writer and publisher, who died in 1843.

Large as the number of donations from individuals to the Library was, the number of books which came from other libraries was very considerably greater, particularly during the earlier years of Balfour's Regius Keepership. The gift from Kew has already been mentioned, as has that from the Trustees of the John Ball Estate and the Trustees of the Hope Estate. Apart from these outstanding gifts and bequests, Balfour received in 1895 some 200 books from the Royal Scottish Arboricultural Society in fulfilment of their promise to the First Commissioner of Works in 1881 that '. . . the Library and Collection of Forest Specimens and Produce belonging to the Society would be deposited for public exhibition and instruction in the event of the establishment of a School of Forestry in Edinburgh Arboretum . . .'[25]

On 1 July 1896 George Murray wrote to Balfour from the British Museum (Natural History): 'I am sending you today a boxful of duplicate books and papers (264 in number) . . .' These books are in the Library, clearly marked 'Ex Bibl. Mus. Brit. 1896' or with an official label fixed to the covers, saying: 'Presented by the Trustees of the British Museum'.

Also in 1896, from the books which Hugh Cleghorn had bequeathed to the Edinburgh University Library, those relating to vegetable products, and plates were sent to Balfour.[26]

Some years later, in 1919, the library of Dr Robert Chapman Davie was bequeathed to the Garden.[27] Davie was on the University staff at the Garden; he died prematurely at the age of 32.[28]

Thus through purchases, exchanges and gifts, Balfour supplied the Library with books and journals. Only about a quarter of the books of his 'Want List' of 1895 was, however, among the books received, but there were among them many extremely valuable ones which Balfour had not included in his list, possibly because they were too expensive even for the time his list was compiled.

Balfour was not a mere collector of books. He wanted them to be available for use by anyone interested in them. By 1893 he had prepared catalogues of the books and journals in the Library.[29] In 1911 a fresh list of the Library's collection of periodicals was published.[30] Some of the library notices and other records of the early years of Balfour at the Garden suggest that there were three separate libraries in the premises: one, his own personal library, which included many books and a large collection of manuscript materials he had inherited from his father which he was to leave in the Garden for the most part; two, the general library for the staff, students and visitors; and three, the workmen's library.[31] Rules and regulations were laid down for the use of the libraries. There was to be no audible conversation or noise of any kind during reading hours. Readers were to see that their hands were clean when using the books. They were to sign the attendance book before leaving the Library and the Regius Keeper would inspect that record every Saturday.

Obviously, there was need for staff to attend to the books in the Library and to see that the rules were observed. Staffing the Library had been a serious problem at the Garden for a long time. Even as far back as 1826 Robert Graham, as noted earlier had spoken about this.[32] Hutton Balfour's repeated petitions to Government to appoint staff to the Herbarium and Library were turned down many times.[33] James McNab, his Principal Gardener, was looking after the Herbarium and Library as best he could until, at last, in 1876 Government agreed to the appointment of a Curator for the Herbarium and Hutton Balfour was able to say that 'Mr F M Webb, the Curator of the Herbarium' would superintend the Library.[34]

Webb died in 1880. No one seems to have replaced him until 1890 when John Hardie Wilson was 'appointed to the Curatorship of the Herbarium and Library of the Royal Botanic Garden, Edinburgh'.[35] There is no record of Wilson's work at the Garden or of the length of his stay there. In any case there was still no member of staff whose sole charge was the Library. This situation did not change during Alexander Dickson's time nor in the early years of Bayley Balfour. In the meantime the collection was growing fast, both in size of stock and value. It was imperative that the Library should have a Librarian and assistants. By 1890 Bayley Balfour had devised a system by which his Clerk, Henry Hastings, would have charge of the Library and a rota was drawn up for one garden employee to act as Librarian for one week at a time.[36] In 1908 Harry Frank Tagg, the Museum Assistant, was put in charge of the Library.[37] He was to have, at first, two temporary assistants, and later, three 'helpers', all of whom were paid 10s. a week.[38]

This was all Bayley Balfour could manage, and he was not happy about it. He wanted someone to be solely in charge of the Library and wrote to the Treasury asking for the post of a Librarian to be approved. There is a letter in the Library archives, dated 16 December 1910, from S K McDonnell of HM Office of Works to the Secretary of HM Treasury which says: 'Dr Balfour does not renew for the present his application for the appointment of an Assistant in the library, although of course he remains strongly of the opinion that such an officer is greatly needed and will eventually have to be appointed if the work in the library is to be carried out properly.' To the force of his arguments, as usual, he added strength through the support of his friends in influential positions. His friends Spring Rice and Bergne had by this time left the Treasury, and he did not have anyone there to plead his case. But he still had the attention and support of R C Munro Ferguson, MP and Sir Kenneth McKenzie of the Exchequer in Edinburgh, both of whom must have played a part in persuading the Treasury in 1912 to assent to the appointment of the first full-time Librarian at the Royal Botanic Garden Library in Edinburgh.[39]

Acquaintance with and love of books were two very important qualities which, Balfour believed, a Librarian must possess. Equally important were erudition, diligence in work and research, facile literary expression and untiring willingness to help others. Balfour knew a man who answered to all these qualities in abundance in the person of Alex P Stevenson, a bookseller in Dundee, who had been of immense service to him in his research into the life and work of George Don, as part of the history of the Botanic Garden.[40] (See also Appendix VI). But, by 1912 when Balfour was ready to appoint his Librarian, Stevenson was not a young man, and the remuneration which went with the job was probably not substantial enough to entice him to uproot himself from his native Dundee. So Balfour had to look elsewhere and decided upon James Todd Johnstone as the first Librarian. Born on 6 April 1883,

> Johnstone, who always maintained that he was descended from Robinson Crusoe, was the son of an antiquarian bookseller from Dumfriesshire. By assisting his father in the bookshop in Dundonald Street, he gained a good knowledge of books, book-binding and printing; as he had studied botany in his University degree (he specialised in Mathematics), he was thus a splendid choice for the Library post which he filled for thirty-five years. For many years he also acted as Assistant Secretary to the Botanical Society and edited its Transactions. And for many years he also edited the Notes from the Royal Botanic Garden Edinburgh . . .[41]

Johnstone was no stranger to the world of books, and his experience and aptitudes must have stood him in good stead in his new position as Librarian. He does not seem to have sought to change much or to introduce new methods and practices. In any case the system in operation was adequate for the purpose of the Garden at the time, and Johnstone simply continued it.

Keeping records of all materials that came to the Library was an important function. This was started by Hutton Balfour soon after the arrival of the Botanical Society Library and carried on by his successors. Johnstone continued to keep these records right up to his retirement in 1946. Thus there is now a record of all that the Library possessed. The later entries in these records, unlike the earlier ones, do not always give dates of receipt of the items nor do they mention if the items were donated or purchased. Every single item that came, be it book, pamphlet, separate, report, or issue of a journal, was given a number and recorded in the register in numerical order. A separate register was kept for exchanges with other libraries and institutions.[42] The Catalogue of Journals of 1911 was kept up-to-date by amendments and additions written in by hand in an interleaved copy. The Author Catalogue was hand-written too, on 6×4 in. index cards, with bibliographical details and cross-references as necessary. There was a large number of analytical entries for monographic papers appearing in various journals.

There was no classification system in use, and no classified catalogue. A classified arrangement of stock was impossible because there was no room. The Library was scattered in different rooms and corridors which were themselves crowded with floor-to-ceiling bookcases and cupboards packed with books and pamphlets and journals of all sizes from Elephant Folios to small octavos. Of necessity, therefore, location had to be fixed, with a self-devised system of numbering the rooms, bookcases and shelves, which were written on the covers of books and journals and their respective catalogue entries. Often there were books which for one reason or another could not be fitted into any bookcases or cupboards; these were 'filed' in the best space available, even if it were 'on top of tea-chest in Room 4'. This location was of course written on the book cover itself and on the catalogue entry.[43]

Johnstone must have enjoyed putting his knowledge of book binding to good use. A great number of books and journals were beautifully bound in different coloured leathers, often with raised bands and gold tooled decorations and lettering of titles on the spines. Johnstone's and his mentor, Balfour's love of books must have been the reason for such lavish binding. The propriety of such expense would be questioned today, but one cannot but admire the beauty of rows of well-bound volumes on the library shelves.

Unlike his predecessors Johnstone's primary and full-time concern was the Library. Possibly there was not enough work to justify the employment of additional assistants. He certainly does not seem to have had any assistance until much later in his career, but this does not mean that Johnstone was not kept busy. Almost immediately after his appointment he was elected Assistant Secretary of the Botanical Society of Edinburgh, a position he held throughout his working life. This meant, among other things, the editing of the Transactions of the Society, seeing it through the press and distributing it. This, as well as the editing and distribution of the Garden's own publication, *Notes from the Royal Botanic Garden Edinburgh*, which Johnstone carried out for many years, must have left him very little time to pursue his own particular research interests. His involvement with publications was not entirely outwith his concern for the Library, because both journals were sent out as exchanges for a large number of publications the Library received.

Apart from editing their Transactions, Johnstone's contribution to the Botanical Society's meetings was limited to an exhibition of a 'series of colour pictures of flowers published by Dr Thornton, c. 1795–1800'.[44] The Society was, however, well pleased with him: at their meeting on 13 March 1947 'The President, on behalf of the Society, presented Mr J T Johnstone with a cheque and referred to his long term of service as Assistant Secretary'.[45]

One paper Johnstone was able to publish was on John Jeffrey and the Oregon Expedition of the 1850s which had its organisational centre at the Garden. The paper outlined the setting up of the association of interested people, and reproduced letters and other documents relating to the Expedition.[46]

Bayley Balfour had always entertained an abiding interest in the history of the Edinburgh Garden and the lives and achievements of its Regius Keepers, Principal Gardeners and others in some way connected with it. He spared no effort to acquire as many original documents or transcripts as he could possibly get from any source. This involved a massive correspondence. All these, as well as the considerable volume of correspondence and papers of his father Hutton Balfour which he had inherited, he preserved with great care, and presented to the Garden after his retirement in 1922. Thus the Library today has most of the primary sources for the history of the Garden.

WILLIAM WRIGHT SMITH

At the end of 34 years of service, when ill-health forced Bayley Balfour to retire from office, there were still many things he wanted to accomplish in and for the Garden. Among the staff there was a gratifying atmosphere of keenness and willingness which augured well for the future.[47] But what gave Balfour even more satisfaction was the appointment of his deputy, William Wright Smith, as his successor. Smith first came to the Garden in 1902 as a member of the University staff under Balfour. He left for India in 1907 and held different botanical posts there until 1911 when Balfour got him back to the Edinburgh Garden as his deputy. So William Wright Smith was no stranger to the Garden and its affairs.

As has been mentioned earlier, at the time of his retirement, Balfour was yet again trying to settle the matter of the library vote. Smith obviously had to take up this correspondence with the Board of Works. He was aware of the difficulties in the matter, but did not have the details of what had happened earlier, to be able to present a case to the Board. Therefore he wrote to Balfour for help.[48] The answer came promptly, tracing the history of the library vote and suggesting the course of action.[49] Smith must have been successful in his arguments with the Board because in a letter Balfour wrote to him on 6 May 1922, he said: 'I am glad the prospect of the library vote is [?secure]'.[50] What actually happened is not clear because in his letter to Smith dated 16 September 1922, Balfour hoped: 'the Board is not worrying you over much about reducing estimates'.

Balfour died in November 1922, only a few months after retirement. His widow, Lady Agnes Balfour, immediately set about sorting out and disposing of her husband's large collection of books and papers. She was in frequent correspondence with Smith in Edinburgh. She wrote to him on 13 February 1923:

> . . . May I send to the garden any pamphlets that are here for the library to select what would be of use and then if you are willing to let the rest go to the Bodleian? Sir Isaac sent a great many there once and they were gratefully received. I am sending you the bound correspondence of Prof. John Hutton Balfour for the library.

Smith replied on 19 February:

> . . . the pamphlets you mention will be very welcome as they are of the greatest service in the library. I will offer the ones we do not retain to the Bodleian in your name. The bound series of correspondence of Prof. John Hutton Balfour will also be treasured . . .

In April 1923 Lady Balfour sent to Smith four cases, with a rough list of their contents of books and papers including some garden accounts for 1794, etc., Botanical Society Club album of scientists, Baillon's *Histoire des Plantes*, Engler's *Pflanzenreich*, Sargent's *Plantae Wilsonianae*, Pfeffer's *Physiology*, and many more bound and unbound books and pamphlets.[51] Smith wrote to Lady Balfour on 25 April 1923:

> . . . The four cases have arrived and I have gone through all the contents. I am very much indebted to you for your kindness in sending so many of Sir Isaac's "working" books to me—I shall treasure them much for their associations as well as for their great usefulness. The volumes of Bentham & Hooker's *Genera Plantarum* are very welcome as I have been trying to get a set for some time for the use of the Herbarium. I put its value at £7. 10s. For it and several other volumes which will be most

useful, may I suggest a payment of £16. For those you have so generously given to me I am very grateful . . .

Thus the Garden Library started well under William Wright Smith's regime. However, there is a dearth of evidence for what progress Smith himself was able to bring about for the Library during his long period in office. After his death, Smith's files at Inverleith House were sifted and burnt by clerical staff from the Ministry of Public Buildings and Works, and most of his papers on administrative matters were thus lost. Much of his correspondence with Kew, especially on exchange and loan of plant specimens for herbarium work and more particularly for the purposes of the *Botanical Magazine* has, however, survived. Among this are some letters which give a glimpse of how the Library fared under Smith.

He exercised strict control over the use made of the Garden Library books. Dr William Burns, on leave from India, while staying in Crieff wanted a loan of Bentham and Hooker's *British Flora* and Hayward's *Botanist's Pocket Book* to help him identify some of the copious flora he found himself surrounded with. Smith answered Burns on 2 June 1925: 'It is not possible for me to lend books from the Government Library as I have no power to do so in accordance with the Government rules.' But Smith's own copy of Hayward and also a copy of White's *Flora of Perthshire* were sent to Burns.

In 1925 Edinburgh had sent to Kew *Lists of plants in flower for 1924* which Kew had somehow mislaid. When this was brought to Smith's attention, he was polite, but very firm in his letters to Kew asking for the return of the lists.

Smith maintained a very close and friendly relationship with Kew. Apart from the unhesitating co-operation with scientific work of the herbarium, much time and effort was spent on the preparation of illustrations and descriptions for the *Botanical Magazine*, the editorial work of which was at that time centred on Kew. On occasion too, Smith sent to Kew publications which he could spare; in 1934, for example, copies of *Flore Illustrée du nord de la Chine, Contributions from the Laboratory of Botany, National Academy of Peiping* and extracts from the *Bulletin Trimestrial de la Société Mycologique de France*.

In 1939 when the needs of the Second World War threatened the publications of Kew and Edinburgh, Smith joined forces with Sir Arthur Hill, Director of Kew, in an effort to save the publications. Hill wrote to Smith on 1 November 1939: 'I think it would be most unwise to stop the issue of scientific publications, especially when they enable both our institutions to get so many periodicals by way of exchange.' Smith agreed completely and added in his letter to Hill dated 6 November 1939:

> . . . The Stationery Office is having its own difficulties. One of the chief troubles will be the supply of paper and there is every likelihood of some of the paper being of a very inferior quality. I think it would be a great pity if your publications and ours were continued on paper which would not fit in well with previous issues. For that reason I would be quite prepared to cut down the actual amount of text or, alternatively, to cut out papers that are not urgent provided that what they do publish is kept up to a reasonable standard as regards paper quality. As long as we have something to send to other institutions, these latter will quite understand a marked reduction in quantity.

As regards the Seed List, I think we can simplify that considerably, but

I do not like to forego the issue of a list which can of course be much restricted. The Stationery Office is now issuing agricultural and other leaflets which are being done by a special process which does not need setting up for printing. I believe the Stationery Office would agree to make up an amended Seed List in this style and it could go out as a 6- or 8-page leaflet without covers. That I think would appeal to them on the side of economy. Perhaps you would care to make use of that suggestion. I believe the list could be typed in a special way and then after that nothing more is necessary but putting the copy through a duplicating machine. I do not know how this is worked, but I understand that it means no great cost in comparison with printing.

The representations made by Kew and Edinburgh were only partly successful because although the 'Bulletin' from Kew was published to 1941 and the 'Notes' from Edinburgh to 1940, both were suspended for the rest of the duration of the War. The number of copies of each issue published was considerably restricted and their distribution very carefully monitored, saving as many copies as possible for distribution to important customers after the War was over. Somehow Edinburgh did not receive its customary two copies of *Kew Bulletin* nos 5, 6 and 7 which Smith came to know were published only from references to them in the literature. Letters flowed to and fro between Kew, Edinburgh and the Stationery Office, and the missing numbers were sent to Edinburgh so that two complete sets of the publication could be kept there.

Financial constraints imposed during and for a period after the War restricted Smith's freedom to do much for the Library at the Garden. He was pleased to receive from Kew a second copy of Hutchinson & Dalziel's *Flora of West Tropical Africa,* copies of some numbers of Edinburgh's own 'Notes' which Kew had received from the library of Mr Grove and which Edinburgh was short of, Hooker's *Icones Plantarum,* and vols 50–54 of *Annalen des Naturhistorischen Museum* which Kew had received from Dr Rechinger in Vienna. Smith was in no position to send any books to Kew or anywhere else, but when he received the two volume set of his old pupil Wen-Pei Fang's *Icones Plantarum Omeiensium,* 1945, from China he sent the volumes to Kew on loan for them to see and for their *Index Kewensis.*

From what can be ascertained from staff and students at the Garden who remember Smith, it would seem that he left the running of the Library largely to Johnstone, who by that time was well and truly established as Librarian and capable of managing the Library in the traditions established by Bayley Balfour. Exchanges were kept up, a few books and journals were bought when absolutely necessary and the accession register was continued. But there was no great enthusiasm to search for and acquire special materials to enrich the resources of the Library. One aspect which seems to come out clearly is that most of the few purchases made were through the Stationery Office and the rest were paid for from University funds. The Stationery Office did not operate with the same liberality they used to show to Balfour. They were acting merely as agents of the Board of Works who had set a ceiling on the amount the Garden Library could spend on purchases of books and journals.

So, Smith's apparent lack of enthusiasm for the Library was perhaps due to the shortage of funds. Added to this difficulty was the equally serious problem of accommodation for any large increase in the number of books. While discussions on the transfer of botanical collections from the Royal Scottish Museum to the Botanic Garden were in progress Smith wrote to the Board of Works on 28 November 1928:

> I need hardly emphasise the importance of a combination of a botanic garden, a botanical library, a herbarium and a botanical museum. The full value of each can only be secured when they are associated. Our herbarium, the most valuable outside London, is housed in an old building used a century ago for flower shows by the local Horticultural Society. The library accommodation is far from adequate either for the visits of the public or for the proper arrangement of the books. It seems to me therefore, well worth consideration that the whole of the problem should be solved by the erection of one adequate building which would accommodate museum materials, library and herbarium. All three are shorn of the greater part of their usefulness when separated from each other as they are at present.

The Board, however, was not impressed. Discussions dragged on for years and in the end Smith had to accept the situation and receive the botanical collections from the Royal Scottish Museum. F J E Raby of the Board of Works wrote on 3 March 1938: 'It has been ascertained from the Regius Keeper that space is available in the existing accommodation at the Royal Botanic Garden for the storage of material proposed to be transferred. The Board accordingly see no objection to the proposal'.

The collection referred to above contained mostly museum exhibits, which were promptly put away in the two museum huts in the Garden. Museum pieces were not, however, the only collection the Scottish Museum was giving up. It was wanting to dispose of the entire Cleghorn Memorial Library and all books relating to botany, forestry and allied subjects in its Library. Introducing a list of this collection of books, printed and published in 1897,[52] the then Director of the Museum, Maj.-Gen. R Murdoch Smith said:

> This list has been compiled for the use of Students and Readers visiting the Library. It contains references not only to the books, but also to some of the more important articles relating to Botany and Forestry in the Library. Works dealing purely with Agriculture have not been included. Section VIII contains a catalogue of the Cleghorn Memorial Library—a collection of books relating chiefly to Forestry. This collection consists partly of works bequeathed to the Library of the Museum by the late Dr Hugh Cleghorn, of Stravithie, Fife, formerly Chief Conservator of Forests in India, and partly of works purchased with money raised as a Memorial Fund by a number of Dr Cleghorn's friends. The united collection, which is of a very valuable character, is now available for reference . . .

By the time the Scottish Museum had decided to hand over this collection to the Botanic Garden, it had grown considerably to some 4,000 volumes. The arrival of these books in 1941 was the biggest event in the history of the Library. Not only did it swell the stock to bursting point, it added immeasurably to the quality and value of the Library, because among the books that arrived were many classics and extremely rare works which the Garden could never have hoped to acquire. The Garden and the Library were fortunate in having a friend like Dr Cleghorn who, first through the Botanical Society and later directly, gifted more books than any other single individual during his life time.[53]

The sudden influx of a vast number of books created serious problems for Johnstone who was directly concerned with their accession and incorporation into stock, not to mention their accommodation. It must have been a long and tiring task which he had to get through with only very little help from assistants who were assigned to him from time to time. Not long after the work was done, in 1946 at the age of 63, he retired from active service. It was arranged that he should come to the Library for a few hours every day, presumably to supervise the work of his assistant who was now running the Library. However, he was not able to do much, and after some time he stopped attending the Library altogether. He died on 19 March 1953.

Johnstone had the help of four successive assistants, more or less regularly, during his time at the Library. The earliest was Marion A C Jockel who came to the Garden in 1914 and stayed until 1937 when she married and went to live in the United States of America. E B V Sloan, a graduate, was the second assistant. She joined the Garden staff in 1937 and later married H R Fletcher, a member of the scientific staff at the Garden who was to succeed Smith in 1956 as Regius Keeper. There is little information on Margaret Torence who is reported to have been Johnstone's assistant for some time. A personal recollection of Johnstone and of the Library at that time is given by Mrs Betty Fletcher (née Sloan) who was Johnstone's assistant from 1937–42. (See Appendix VII).

When it was known that Johnstone planned to retire in July 1946 Smith does not seem to have tried very hard to get a replacement. This apparent lack of enthusiasm may have been due to the refusal of the Ministry of Works (as the Board of Works had come to be known) to sanction the post. The difficulty with the Ministry was, possibly, the discussions taking place at the time on the staffing levels at the Kew and Edinburgh gardens, as well as other departments under the Government. Before they would approve the appointment of the replacement for Johnstone, they wanted the on-going discussion between the departments, the institutions and the Institution of Professional Civil Servants to be completed and guidelines on establishment and grading of staff based on comparabilities agreed upon.

Whatever the situation was, Smith had no doubt at all about the necessity for someone to be in charge of the Library when Johnstone left. This might well have been in Smith's mind when in January of 1946 he moved Dorothea E Purves, who had been an assistant in the Garden from 1944, to work beside Johnstone. When Johnstone retired in July, Smith simply asked Purves to take over. By then she had picked up the well-established traditions and routines of the Library and continued to operate them. In case of difficulty Johnstone was available, at least for the initial period. Both the relatively small number of Garden staff and the considerably larger number of University staff and students were well accustomed to the way of the Library. Neither group found any difference in the service they received and no complaints were made. So matters continued as usual.

Perhaps Smith wanted to improve the staffing in the Library. He seems to have succeeded to the point of getting the Treasury to conduct an inspection in 1951, although the inspectors did not recommend any change.

These were the conditions when Brian Lawrence Burtt came to the Garden in July 1951 as a Principal Scientific Officer from the Royal Botanic Gardens in Kew. Even at that time he was a botanist of repute, and very interested in and knowledgeable about botanical literature and bibliography. He was the obvious man for Smith to turn to for advice on the Library. As the Regius Keeper, D M Henderson, said at an open meeting of the staff in 1979, to Burtt was due in large measure the credit for the professional staffing and reorganisation of the Library in the mid-1950s, paving the way for later developments. Burtt's first concerns were the Herbarium and botanical research. Nevertheless, he was constantly trying to improve the condition of the Library. It was his persistence which led to the second Treasury inspection of the Library in 1955. This time the inspectors recommended the appointment of a temporary, professional Librarian. The first person selected to this post was J Marguerite Alford, a graduate in botany and a chartered librarian. Purves continued in the library under Alford, who also had the part-time assistance of a Laboratory Attendant, Karl Ekeval.

Immediately upon taking charge of the Library, Alford began the reorganisation of the stock by introducing modern methods of librarianship. She chose the Bliss Bibliographical Classification system, with modifications to suit the particular needs of the Garden, and more especially to match the arrangement of the books in the Library to that of the specimens in the Herbarium. Obviously she needed the four volumes in three of the Bliss Schedules and Index, second edition, 1952, to do the job. When the volumes arrived and Smith, then already an octogenarian saw them, he could not understand why they were bought, and so sent them to Burtt with a note: 'Mr Burtt—To see these volumes before passing to the Library. Please look at them and tell me why in all the world we bought them; I hardly consider that they will be a gift. I cannot remember, however, agreeing to their purchase. WWS 30.4.56'. Burtt, of course, explained the necessity for the volumes and Smith was pacified and sent a note: '. . . Thank you very much indeed for your note regarding the volumes I sent on to you. This explains why I was really puzzled . . .'

Whatever difficulties he might have had with the Garden Library, like all his predecessors in office, Smith, too, kept his own library. Many of his books bearing his signature are in the Library today.

Sir William Wright Smith died in office on 15 December 1956, just a few weeks before his 82nd birthday.

HAROLD ROY FLETCHER

Soon after William Wright Smith's death in 1956 the two posts of Regius Keeper of the Garden and Regius Professor of Botany of the University of Edinburgh, both of which had been held by the same person at any given time for well over two centuries, were separated. Harold Roy Fletcher was appointed as Regius Keeper, and Professor Robert Brown as Regius Professor of Botany. However, the University Department stayed at the Garden until 1965 when it was moved to the University site at King's Buildings. Even then the Taxonomy Section of the Department remained at the Garden, where it still remains, with its professor and his staff and research students.

When Fletcher took charge as Regius Keeper, Alford was well into her professional stride, recataloguing and classifying the Library stock. The task was not simple, nor was there any quick way of completing it. The stock of some 35,000 volumes she had to examine, record and arrange was a difficult collection of very old and new works, many of them rare and very valuable, and of varying sizes. The lack of space did not make her attempt at a classified arrangement any easier. Nevertheless, like a true and dedicated professional she carried on. She certainly needed and asked for professional assistance; but it was a long time coming.

In the meantime, in 1958, Fletcher received a letter from Christmas Humphrys, Chairman of the Society of Herbalists in London, offering the magnificent library of the Society to the Botanic Garden in Edinburgh for a very modest sum. The library had been built up over a period of years by Mrs Carl Frederick Leyel,[54] the pioneer herbalist and founder of the Society of Herbalists. Fletcher jumped at the opportunity to enrich the Library at the Garden beyond all expectations and lost no time in assessing the value of the collection—of which Burtt, after an examination of the books, assured Fletcher—and approaching the Ministry for funds. Letters relating to this clearly suggest that the Ministry was interested in the offer. The Society, however, withdrew the first offer and decided to sell only a small part of their library.[55] From the books on offer, Alford selected four, at a total price of £1,510. These were: Georg Christian von Oeder, *Flora Danica* . . . (1761–1883), 17 vols, folio; James Sowerby, *English Botany* . . . (1790–1814), 36 vols, plus Supplements 1–5 (1831–1863); Franz de Paula Adam Graf von Waldstein and Paul Kitaibel, *Descriptiones et Icones Plantarum rariorum Hungariae* (1799–1812), 3 vols, folio; and Ambroise Marie Francoise Joseph Palisot de Beauvois, *Flore d' Oware et de Bénin, en Afrique* (1804–1807), 2 vols, folio.

In the following year the Library received a collection of some 130 books and journals, including some scarce Russian Floras, from Peter H Davis of the University staff at the Garden in charge of the taxonomy section and the Flora of Turkey Project.

Malcolm Wilson was the Mycologist on the University staff at the Garden. '. . ."His classes were well taught and happily taught"; taught by example as well as by precept how to seek out information, how to use libraries and herbaria'.[56] He retired in 1951. When he died in 1960, his books, correspondence and other personal papers were sent to the Garden by his widow.

The perennial difficulty in staffing the Library adequately was continuing in the meantime. The response of the Treasury to the representations made on this matter was a staff inspection in 1959 which resulted only in the confirmation of the temporary post of librarian. This was a step forward, but did little to lessen the work-load. In fact, the situation deteriorated because Purves, whose experience was of no small help to Alford in the day to day running of the Library, was transferred in 1960 to the Plant Records Office. The linguist who replaced her, by name Prior, had no experience of library work at all so that he needed training and supervision. In any case, he resigned from the Garden employment within seven months to take up a university course. So Alford was left virtually on her own. Naturally very little progress could be made in reorganisation. Burtt, who was the supervisor of the Library, discussed the unhappy situation with Fletcher and a strong case was presented to the Ministry requesting more staff, including a professional assistant. Agard

Evans, the Chief Librarian of the Ministry in London, supported the case and the Treasury agreed to the appointment of a professional Assistant Librarian. All this, of course, took time, and by the time the new assistant, Hugh A Colquhoun was appointed in September 1961, Alford had already decided to leave. She left in November. So the Library was again in difficulties. However, Fletcher acted swiftly and in December 1961 William Hunter Brown came in as Librarian.

Because of the interminable difficulties the Library had had to contend with over a long time, especially in the areas of staffing and accommodation, it was not surprising that Brown found the condition of the Library far from satisfactory (Appendix VIII). He had a tremendous task ahead of him. Unlike his predecessors, he had a professional assistant right from the start, and frequently, part-time assistants. There was also the new Herbarium and Library building in the planning stages, which when completed, would solve the accommodation problem and provide very congenial conditions in which to work. With such assistance at hand and prospect for the future, Brown took up the job of reorganising the Library where Alford had left off.

Time was short because the Library was to be moved to its new accommodation early in 1964 in time for the Tenth International Botanical Congress which was to be held in Edinburgh in August of that year. It was important to present to the hundreds of delegates from all over the world a well organised and efficiently run library as an integral part of a Botanic Garden of international renown.

Brown was not without his share of difficulties. Constant staff changes impeded the progress of his work. His assistant, Colquhoun, was transferred on temporary promotion to the Ministry's other library in Edinburgh for seven months. The vacancy was filled by the temporary appointment of Agnes W Laidlaw. Transfers, retirements and replacements also occurred frequently among his other staff. Although Brown was not short of his full complement of assistants for any length of time, the arrival and departure of staff did not contribute towards an uninterrupted flow of work.

Not only had Hunter Brown to see to the cataloguing and classification, he also had to arrange for the binding and repair of stock which had been neglected for many years. Through Fletcher, he persuaded HM Stationery Office to allocate extra funds and facilities to have large numbers of periodicals bound and other volumes professionally restored.

In 1962 Professor Brown wanted all university books and journals in the Garden Library to be separated and put together as the University Botany Library, under its own Librarian appointed by the University. The University had been buying books for the Garden Library for a number of years, and by no means had all those books been marked as University property; this was particularly true of several journals. The separation of stock was, therefore, another difficult job Hunter Brown had to attend to.

Increasing number of accessions was yet another problem. Fletcher was gradually accelerating purchases through the Stationery Office. The number of books and journals received as donations and exchanges was far greater. There were also some other gifts and bequests which contained large collections of archival and photographic materials which called for special treatment, and hence more of Brown's time.

On 5 August 1962, an old friend of the Garden, Captain Richard D Trotter of Flichity, Inverness, wrote to Fletcher offering to exchange his set of Pierre-Joseph Redoute's *Les Liliacées*, 8 vols, folio (1802–1816) for the Garden's own set of the work. The set of the celebrated botanical artist's work which had been left to Trotter by the well known horticulturist, Edward Augustus Bowles, was in a much better condition than the Garden's own rather worn set. Moreover, Trotter's set had the added attraction of containing all the monochrome plates besides the coloured plates (Plate 2). Fletcher had no difficulty in obtaining the Ministry's permission to effect the exchange.[57] Trotter, however, did not stop with the exchange. He had the set he received from the Garden suitably rebound and sold it. The proceeds were used to purchase Nikolaus Joseph Baron von Jacquin, *Icones Plantarum rariorum*, 3 vols, folio (1781–1795), for the Garden Library.[57]

In 1963, the wife of the Edinburgh trained, British botanist Frederick Robert Irvine,[58] who had spent most of his working life in Africa and died there in 1962, sent to Edinburgh all her husband's botanical books and papers, including his diaries and the large card index of his work on edible plants. The collection contained 298 books, 1,100 reprints and 550 parts of journals. In the same year 120 volumes of books and journals were presented to the Edinburgh Garden by the Director of the Royal Botanic Gardens, Kew.

Palaeontologist Dr Elizabeth M Knox's collection of books and papers on fossil botany was presented to the Garden in early 1964. She was an active member of the Botanical Society of Edinburgh, and its President in 1949. Some of her papers were published in the Society's Transactions.[59]

A more valuable and significant addition to the Garden Library in that year was the bequest of Dr Joseph F Rock.[60] Apart from being a taxonomic botanist of note, he was a talented linguist and writer, distinguished traveller and recognised authority on China. His bequest consisted of a very large collection of some 40,000 photographs, diaries and manuscripts. Under the terms of Rock's will, his collection was to be shared by the Royal Botanic Garden in Edinburgh and the Deutsche Morgenländische Gesellschaft in Berlin. Discussions on the matter resulted in Edinburgh keeping about half of the photographs and all original diaries and manuscripts and the DMG receiving transcripts and certain papers of no botanical interest.

The new Herbarium and Library Building was making good progress, and was expected to be ready for occupation early in 1964. With the staff at his disposal Brown was not able to guarantee that the Library would be fully ready for the move at the expected time. So, when Colquhoun returned to the Garden at the end of his period of secondment to the Ministry Library at Saughton, Laidlaw who was standing in for him was allowed to continue as an additional Assistant Librarian to help with the preparation of the Library for the move. She worked in the Library till 30 April 1964.

The actual transfer of the Library to its new quarters took place in April 1964, and Brown was able to report:

> The general state of the library is now excellent but a number of long-term tasks remain to be done notably the gradual retyping of the catalogue and incorporation into stock of the various bequests of the past two years which now include about 6,000 reprints. More immediate tasks include the amendment of the existing catalogue to remove old location marks and a certain amount of reclassifying to produce a better

shelf order. In addition, 8,500 volumes have still to be provided with class-marks . . . The use of the library has been made considerably easier by the bringing together for the first time of the entire stock into a single sequence. University staff continue to make unrestricted use of the collection but all undergraduate student borrowing is now channelled through the departmental librarian . . .[61]

Soon the preparations for the big event of the year gathered momentum. International Botanical Congresses are held every six years, and are of immense importance to the botanical world. That the Tenth Congress was being held in Edinburgh was a matter of pride as much for the Garden as for the city, and the nation. The Post Office commemorated the occasion by issuing a set of stamps, appropriately with botanical themes. The Congress which was held in August was, by all accounts, a grand success.

Needless to say, the brand new, purpose built Herbarium and Library, opened by Her Majesty Queen Elizabeth II in June of that year, attracted considerable attention from the large number of delegates to the Congress, both British and foreign. The gleaming Library (Fig. 20) was a show-piece, the cause of envy to many.

After the Congress some interesting gifts were received. Besides the several books sent in by individuals such as Viola E Craigs Cowan of Tobermory in the

20. The RBG Library in 1984.

Isle of Mull, who sent a copy of John Parkinson's *Theatrum Botanicum* (1640), there were somewhat larger collections received from: Rev. N Dennis, SJ, in Kirkwall, Orkney; W G Martin of Edinburgh; the library of J T Jeffrey who was the Superintendent of Parks in Edinburgh; and Flora Murray through her solicitors in Edinburgh. Among these collections were: Philip Miller's *Gardener's Dictionary* (1752); J C Loudon's *Encyclopaedia of Gardening* (1822); *Horticultural Register*, vols 1–5 (1832–1836); *Journal of Horticulture*, 1883–1885; *Pomologist*, 1866–1871; and Loudon's *Hortus Britannicus* (1839). Sir James Justice's *British Gardener's new Director* (1765) was gifted by J Robertson Justice, actor and descendant of the author.

In 1965 Professor Brown and his entire University Department, except the Taxonomy Section, but including the Departmental Library, moved to the new University site at King's Buildings. Although thus physically removed, relationship between the two places remained cordial. The separation of the libraries affected both the Garden and University staff, the latter more adversely. This was particularly true in regard to access to periodical literature. It was, therefore, inevitable that the University had to borrow heavily from the Garden. The situation has not changed; the University continues to be by far the largest borrower from the Garden Library.

After the Botanical Congress and the transfer of the Botany Department, the Garden had to adjust to the new normality. There were, of course, plenty of matters to engage the attention of all staff. Despite the new accommodation and the incomparably better working conditions there was a great deal to be done to make the Library as well managed and administered as it deserved. At the beginning of 1965 the Library had 24,477 volumes of journals and 16,975 volumes of books, making a total stock of 41,452 volumes. 764 current periodical titles were received through purchase and exchange. There were some 5,000 reprints, and most of the bequests of recent years waiting to be sorted, catalogued, classified and incorporated into stock; the large stock of duplicates had to be examined and dealt with; the mass of invaluable archival material had to be sorted, recorded and arranged for use; the big accumulation of binding and repair work had to be cleared. With the staff help he had, Brown could only just cope with the day to day business of the Library; there was no way he could have attempted to tackle the backlog of work from years past. The help of library school students who worked in the Library from time to time as part of their training and studies, was only a mixed blessing, which did not and could not be expected to make any significant improvement in the situation.

Obviously Hunter Brown needed more staff, both professional and clerical. Not only that; as Librarian of a highly specialised library of national importance, he deserved a higher grading of his position. Fletcher had no hesitation in fully supporting Brown's claims and putting them forward to the Ministry. The resulting staff inspection in 1966 recommended a somewhat improved staff structure, with a Librarian in charge, an Assistant Librarian, a Clerical Officer, a Clerical Assistant and a Typist. On the question of the Librarian's grading the inspectors were unable to recommend an up-grading, but accepted that he had more responsibility than his counterparts elsewhere in the Civil Service, and so granted a special responsibility allowance to be attached to the salary of the Librarian of the Royal Botanic Garden in Edinburgh.

GLORIOSA SUPERBA; THE SUPERB GLORIOSA.

Plate 5. Plate from Mrs James Cookson's Flowers drawn and painted in India. 60×44 cm.

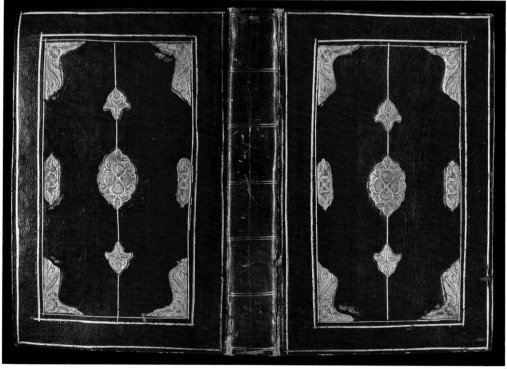

Plate 6. Decorations on the binding of Robert Eliot's Hortus Siccus. 31×22 cm. Persian style binding of MS notes taken at John Hope's lectures. 20.5×13.5 cm.

The outcome of the staff inspection was obviously not altogether encouraging, particularly to Brown or, indeed, to his assistant Colquhoun. Within three months, in July 1966, Colquhoun left to take up appointment as Librarian at the Royal Naval Engineering College in Manadan, Plymouth. Laidlaw, who had worked in the Library before, was again appointed temporarily to replace Colquhoun to the end of the year. Apart from student assistants, Brown does not seem to have had a fully qualified assistant in 1967, and library staffing was again showing signs of falling badly behind, with all its consequences, not least of which was loss of staff morale. Brown was, naturally, very disappointed. His ambitions for the Library and for himself were not going to be achieved. He left the Library on 30 August 1967 to take up appointment as Deputy Librarian of the Heriot-Watt University in Edinburgh.

Brown's departure from the Library did not sever his connection with the Garden. For some time before he left, he had been assisting Fletcher in researching the long history of the Garden. The early part of the history had been thoroughly researched, documented and written principally by Bayley Balfour and John McQueen Cowan.[62] However, in view of the tercentenary of the foundation of the Garden coming up in 1970, it was appropriate that the whole 300 year history was put together. So even after he left the Library, Brown was often in the Garden, working with Fletcher. Their History was published on the occasion of the tercentenary.[63]

M V Mathew (alias Mathew Vareed Manjil) took charge as Librarian on 20 November 1967. He was a chartered librarian with graduate and post-graduate qualifications from the University of Madras in India and from the School of Librarianship in Manchester. He came to the Garden from the Scottish Office Library which he had joined in 1965. Prior to that he was in an industrial research library near Nottingham, and Central Public Library in Leeds. Before coming to Britain he was the Librarian of the St Thomas' College, Trichur, Kerala, India. At the time of his arrival at the Garden, there was Barbara Fairweather as temporary Assistant Librarian, who wanted to go to the library in Kew as soon as she passed the qualifying examination. Harriet S Boyes had just been promoted to Clerical Officer from the position of Clerical Assistant-cum-Typist. Irene H Farquhar was Clerical Assistant and Margaret Cormack was Typist. Fletcher was engrossed in writing the History. Burtt was still very interested in the Library but was no longer officially its supervisor. That position was held by D M Henderson who was away on a world study tour of Botanical Gardens and research institutions. So Mathew was left much to his own devices.

It did not take him long to realise that despite the new accommodation and congenial working conditions there was an enormous amount of work waiting to be done. He realised, too, that there was no possibility of getting any additional assistance because only recently had the staff complement been decided by the Treasury.

The day-to-day running of the Library, assisting the Garden staff and visitors with their enquiries, and attending to the correspondence were enough to fill most of the day. Whatever spare time was available was spent in selecting items for purchase in which Henderson was a great help. Mycology which was his specialism and other obvious Floras and general garden literature were no problem. For other specialised literature Burtt and others in special subject areas were happily free with their advice. All purchases were through the

Stationery Office who sent out the orders to publishers or booksellers, paid the bills and kept the accounts. The only concern was to accession the books and journals as they came in and process them for incorporation into stock.

Bayley Balfour had made a point of providing as good a library service as he could manage for the students in the Garden. Indeed, the students and other Garden staff were encouraged to use the Library. The story goes that if any of them failed to come to the Library for a number of days—a fact he could verify by examining the library attendance register—they would be asked why. This concern for the students seems not to have been noticeable during Smith's time, nor in the years that followed. In the late 1960s student gardeners were severely restricted in the use of the Library. Henderson was in total agreement that these restrictions should be lifted and everyone allowed free use of the Library and its services. This immediately increased the regular clientele of the Library by some 50 people. The only regulation imposed was that loans to these users would be recorded separately so that when they were leaving the Garden a check could be made to ensure that there were no loans due from them, and a 'No Dues' certificate issued.

Gifts and exchanges continued to be the primary source for additions to the stock. Under this category were also many books sent by various authors and publishers for review by the professional staff at the Garden. Aslib sent books for 'Annotations' which would be published in their regular Book Lists. In August 1969 a miscellaneous collection of about 200 books, pamphlets, reprints and issues of journals was received from the library of J Thomas Swarbrick in Ayr. He was for some time the Director of the Scottish Horticultural Research Institute in Dundee. The collection included such items as: Olov Hedberg, *Afroalpine vascular plants, a taxonomic revision* (1957); J C Loudon, *Encyclopaedia of Gardening* (1835 edition), and some volumes of *Conspectus Florae Angolensis*.

Library finance was by no means princely, but it was a good deal better than in the earlier years. In 1968 the Stationery Office began to delegate to the various Government departments the responsibility for the purchase of books priced £4. or under. This necessitated the operation of a Stationery Office vote and a direct purchase vote, which in turn obliged the Library to keep accounts of the latter. This delegation of responsibility to departments is now complete. Government libraries need no longer purchase anything through the Stationery Office. This freedom to act independently has brought with it the responsibility for keeping all accounts and paying bills.

Extension of full library services to students brought to light their particular needs which could not be met with the money allocated for that purpose. This was where the refreshing attitude of the new Chief Librarian of the Ministry in London, C David Overton, proved very helpful. When he visited Edinburgh the need for better staffing and financing of the Library was impressed upon him. He could not do much about staffing immediately, but for the purchase of books he introduced a system by which lists of books required for the horticultural students were sent to him in London and he would obtain the books from his own vote and send them to Edinburgh. This was a very acceptable arrangement, and was the forerunner of the present provision for the supply of text-books to students at subsidised prices.

Overton was also sympathetic to the Library's special need to buy expensive rare works in a hurry when they came on the market. He was prepared to persuade the Treasury to allocate an agreed sum every year for this specific purpose. Any sum not spent in any year would automatically be added to the sum allocated in the following year, thus allowing for the possibility of a substantial sum being built up for any really expensive purchases.

The Library's financial resources were looking up and more and better acquisitions were coming within its grasp, when responsibility for the Garden was devolved from the Ministry of Public Buildings and Works in London to the Scottish Office in Edinburgh in 1969. The Scottish Office had had a covetous eye on the Garden for a long time, certainly from the days of Bayley Balfour.[64] However, the immediate cause for the transfer was, very likely, the ascendancy of Scottish Nationalism which was evident at the time.

Understandably there was apprehension at the Garden about the effect of the change of masters. But the Garden need not have feared. Fletcher submitted a memorandum to the new superiors, outlining the state of the Garden and what he wanted for the future. The Library, indeed, featured in the memorandum (Appendix IX). The response of the Secretary for the Department of Agriculture & Fisheries for Scotland was the appointment of a Scientific Review Group to enquire into the affairs of the Garden and report with recommendations for its development. The Review Group's recommendations were very much along the lines Fletcher had wanted, and paved the way for the developments that were to take place in the following years.

In the meantime the Garden was preparing for the celebration of the tercentenary of its foundation. In June 1970 there was a week of various functions and activities to mark the occasion, attended by scores of delegates from a number of botanic gardens, universities and research institutions scattered all over the world. A major function was a Symposium on the flora and vegetation of south-west Asia, sponsored by the Botanical Society of Edinburgh. Papers presented at this were published in 1971.[65] Besides the Garden's history an *Index of Collectors*[66] was also published at the time of the tercentenary. The Library has preserved the hundreds of congratulatory addresses received on the occasion. Many of them have elaborately painted and decorated botanical emblems and symbols, and are a joy to behold.

At this time Katherine S Milne was the temporary Assistant Librarian. She had joined the staff in January 1970, succeeding Jean Wood who had served in the post from January to September 1969. Barbara Fairweather had left in November 1968.

Fletcher retired from service in August 1970.

NOTES AND REFERENCES

1. The full text of the address, in typescript, is in the archives of the RBG Library, Edinburgh.

2. *Proceedings of the Royal Society of Edinburgh*, Session 1922–1923 vol. 43, pp. 233–234.

3. BEAN, W J (1908). *The Royal Botanic Gardens, Kew: historical and descriptive . . .* London, Cassell & Co., p. xvi.

4. Universities (Scotland) Act, 1889, para. 24 (quoted on pp. 14–15).

5. BEAN, W J (1908). *The Royal Botanic Gardens, Kew: historical and descriptive . . .* London, Cassell & Co., pp. 31, 34 and 42.

6. *Proc. Roy. Soc. Edinb.* Session 1922–1923, vol. 43, p. 233.

7. First draft of the Report of the Committee appointed to enquire into the position of the Regius Keeper of the Botanic Garden, Edinburgh . . . 1890. Section on the Library (In West Register House, Edinburgh, File Ref. MV. 3/102).

8. Sir Isaac Bayley Balfour's letter dated 25 April 1922 to his successor in Edinburgh, Prof. William Wright Smith, recalled how he got the first £30. allowance for the library:

> . . . Dyer told me that when Spring Rice came to him with my proposals supported more or less as you will see by the board Dyer said—"Oh, give him £30."! Spring Rice was from the Treasury!

9. These books are listed in the register of donations to the library.

10. W T Thiselton-Dyer's letter of 21 January, 1890 in West Register House, Edinburgh, File Ref. MW. 3/115:

> . . . with regard to the herbarium and library, as you, I think, rightly assent to the principle, I need say nothing more than that here also I think the principle of specialisation might be introduced . . .
>
> I have already sent Prof. Balfour some books mostly from the library of the late Mr Bentham which was placed at our disposal.

11. Report of the Committee appointed to enquire into the position of the Regius Keeper of the Botanic Garden, Edinburgh . . . 1890. Section (d) Library. (In the RBG Library, Edinburgh). The first draft of this report (see Ref. 7 above) gives very much more detail.

12. *Transactions and Proceedings of the Botanical Society of Edinburgh*, 1893, vol. 19, p. 3.

Numerous presents to the Library, the Museum, and the Herbarium at the Royal Botanic Garden were announced.*

> The PRESIDENT directed the attention of the Society to the exceptional extent and value of the presents of books—some of which were exhibited—recently added to the Library. The greater part of the presents came from the Library of the late Mr John Ball, FRS, well known as an Alpine traveller and botanist, who, dying October 21, 1889, bequeathed his Herbarium and Botanical Library "to Sir Joseph Dalton Hooker, the Director of the Royal Botanical Gardens at Kew for the time being, and to the President of the Royal Society of London for the time being, requesting them to give the same Herbarium and Library to such person or persons or public institution in this country, the British Colonies, or elsewhere in the world, as they or any two of them may select, with the sole object of promoting the knowledge of natural science, subject to the condition that the Keeper of the Royal Herbarium at Kew may, in the first place, select any specimens or books that may be desirable for that Institution." Edinburgh Botanic Garden has been so fortunate as to obtain the gift from the trustees. The Library has already been received, and the Herbarium, a very extensive one, will in due course be added to the collection at the Botanic Garden.
>
> *An official list of these will appear in future in the Annual Report upon the Garden by the Keeper, and a list of them will not therefore be printed in the Society's publications.

13. HOOKER, J D: John Ball . . . *Proceedings of the Royal Society of London*, 1889–1890, vol. 47: Obituary notices of Fellows deceased, p. ix.

> His extensive herbarium and botanical library were left by bequest to Sir J D Hooker, the Director of the Royal Gardens, Kew, and the President of this Society, to be dealt with as they think fit, with the sole object of promoting the knowledge of natural science.

14. *List of books from the Botanical Library of the late John Ball, FRS, presented by the Trustees to the Royal Botanic Garden Library, Edinburgh.* The copy of this printed list in the RBG Library, Edinburgh, is incomplete. The last page present is ten, which takes the alphabetical sequence of author's names to the beginning of the letter 'Z', making the number of 'Bound Books' 233. The list must have had some 16 pages, the missing pages mentioning a few more books and a large collection of smaller works such as pamphlets, separates, journals, etc.

15. Register of correspondence with HM Office of Works, London. (In RBG Library, Edinburgh). Entries under dates 20 February 1894 and 1 March 1894.

16. *Ibidem*. Entries under dates 20 April 1894 and 21 May 1894.

17. Letter dated 2 May 1898 from Bayley Balfour to R C Munro Ferguson, MP:

. . . We shall have an allowance of £30 for books and periodicals and for any exceptional bargain to be obtained in Edinburgh which would cause an excess on this I may get permission of the Controller of the SO to purchase. Under this rider I have been able in the past years to get some good books and I have just sent in a demand under it for works costing over £100. I don't know whether I am likely to get them. In the time past the Controller has usually assented to my demand but it has been more moderate.

This Spring I went to the Treasury to raise the question of a larger vote. Spring Rice as you know now reigns instead of Bergne and he has asked to allow the present system to continue for the year which I assented—but before estimates are presented for next year I hope something may be done that will put us in a better position. The £30 we get hardly pays for periodicals . . .

18. Parliamentary Debates, Fourth Series, 1897, vol. 48, col. 877:

Mr MUNRO FERGUSON (Leith Burgh) called attention to the library at the Botanic Garden, Edinburgh, which, he said, was still in an elementary condition. The library at Kew was an excellent botanical library, and there were possibly three or four other libraries in London which are all equally perfect. The one in Edinburgh, however, was not sufficiently perfect for the educational requirements of those who attend the courses of lectures at the Royal Botanical Gardens. We hoped the right hon. Gentleman, when he was next in Edinburgh, would give some attention to the matter. They were very grateful to him for what he had already done by way of the extension of buildings at the Garden, which had been put in a much more satisfactory condition than they had been in hitherto. Of late years the courses of lectures had been much more important both to gardeners and foresters, and the want of a properly equipped library had therefore been very much felt . . .

19. Letter dated 25 April 1922 from Bayley Balfour to William Wright Smith. In the letter Balfour recounts the chronology of the library vote. Balfour's handwriting is not easy to read, but the part where he says '1898 the year when . . . clinched the matter' is clear enough. The letter was written from Balfour's retirement in Haslemere, Surrey, for the immediate help of his successor at the Garden, Wright Smith, who was at that time negotiating the library vote with the Treasury.

20. List of books—with prices—upon Systematic Botany which are not in the Library at the Royal Botanic Garden, Edinburgh—1895. Typescript. (In the RBG Library, Edinburgh).

21. Letter dated 28 May 1898 from Bayley Balfour to Mr R C Munro Ferguson, MP.

. . . I fancy that I have to thank you for the very ready response the Treasury has given to the application I recently made for some books. I am glad to be able to tell you that I have got some very useful books costing no less than £113. and I am very grateful to you for the interest you have taken in our Library.

Of course this does not really supply us in the way we ought to be supplied but having as I told you agreed to continue under the old system for another year I am very glad the Treasury has not shown itself unwilling to be fairly liberal . . .

22. The relative invoices from Dulau & Co., London, dated 14 September 1903 and 2 March 1905 with the addresses of the recipients are in the RBG Library, Edinburgh.

23. Minutes of the Council Meeting of the Botanical Society of Edinburgh, held on 30 December 1890.

24. All letters relating to the gift from Jenner are in the library of the RBG, Edinburgh. Robert Lindsay, Curator of the Garden, and a friend of Jenner, acted on behalf of Jenner. He wrote to Balfour on 28 August 1888:

. . . Mr Charles Jenner intends presenting to the Garden Library a complete copy of the Bot. Mag. He has asked me to procure the work for that purpose and also to arrange for it being supplied for the next 8 or 10 years, he to bear the cost. Quaritch offers a set for £125. I called on Dr Archibald Dickson on Saturday about his brother's copy and found that he had no objection to dispose of it, and have written to Mr

Jenner suggesting as the best way to get a Bookseller to value the work. Dr Dickson is still very weak, his right arm is quite powerless . . .

The set of the *Botanical Magazine* volumes must have been presented to the Garden early in September because on 13 September Jenner was writing to Balfour in response to the latter's note of thanks for the gift:

> . . . Accept kindly my best thanks for your very courteous note that the want of this book was seriously felt at the Garden in the direct interest of your numerous enquiries, myself among the number prompted in me the desire to provide it, and I am the more happy to have done so, as it has won me your letter and also my friend Mr Lindsay's generous thanks . . .

The speed with which the volumes were delivered at the Garden suggest that they were acquired locally from Archibald Dickson and not from Quaritch in London. Archibald Dickson's brother was Alexander Dickson.

25. *Transactions of the Royal Scottish Arboricultural Society*, 1895, vol. 14, part 3, [Proceedings] p. 12.

[At a General Meeting of the Royal Scottish Arboricultural Society held on 26 July 1895]:

> On behalf of the Library Committee, Dr Somerville reported that, in terms of a promise contained in a Memorial presented by the Society to the First Commissioner of Works on 12 March 1881, that the Library and Collection of Forest Specimens and Produce belonging to the Society must be deposited for public exhibition and instruction in the event of the establishment of a School of Forestry in Edinburgh Arboretum, the Committee had handed over to the Curator of the Royal Botanic Garden the specimens and such of the Books as were not already in the Library there, on the condition that the articles should be marked as having been presented by the Society; he also reported that a list of the Articles presented had been put up with the Society's papers.

26. Edinburgh University Library Committee Minutes, 1877–1905.

15 January 1896:

> The Librarian reported that he had spent two of the days of the Christmas holidays in bringing over from Strathvithie a collection of books bequeathed to the library by the late Dr Cleghorn and consisting of works—some of them very valuable and scarce—on Forestry and Botany. He was instructed to ask the advice of Dr Burges and Col. Bailey as to the rejection of any needlessly trivial matter.

12 February 1896: Dr Burges's report on the Cleghorn Collection said that he had set aside books on '. . . vegetable products and plates that will be sent to Prof. Balfour'.

27. The typescript list of the books received in the library is in the RBG Library, Edinburgh.

28. *Trans. Proc. Bot. Soc. Edinburgh*, 1919, vol. 27, pp. 342–344.

29. Printed guides to these catalogues, in use at the time, are in the RBG Library, Edinburgh.

30. This was published as 'Catalogue of Library: A. Periodicals, Transactions of Societies, and the like' in the Garden's own journal, *Notes from the Royal Botanic Garden Edinburgh*, 1911, vol. 6, Nos 26 and 27, pp. 1–126.

31. Among the various notices preserved in the Library at the RBG Edinburgh is one dated 1893 which speaks of loans from the Keeper's Library, another one dated 1890 which speaks of the rules and regulations for the use of the Garden Library and Reading Rooms, and a third one dated 1892 mentions a Workmen's Library.

32. Evidence, oral and documentary . . . London, 1837 (See Chapter 1, pp. 16, 17).

33. Request for staff to look after the Herbarium and Library was a recurring theme in much of Hutton Balfour's correspondence with the Government of the day. These letters are in the archives of the RBG Library, Edinburgh.

34. BALFOUR, John Hutton: Appeal on behalf of the Library . . . (quoted in full on p. 57).

35. MACDONALD, J A (1984). *Plant science & scientists in St Andrews up to the middle of the 20th Century*. St Andrews, p. 9.

36. ROYAL BOTANIC GARDEN AND ARBORETUM, EDINBURGH. Garden Library and Reading Room. Rules and Regulations . . .

> 7. The Clerk shall have charge of, and be responsible for the safety of the Books, etc., in the Library and Reading room, and for the proper conduct of those who use it. A Librarian for the week shall be appointed from among the Employees . . . March 1890.

37. Library Notice dated September 1908:

> The block of buildings including Lecture Hall, Laboratories, Museum, Library is in charge of Mr Tagg. Lecturers, Assistants, and students who wish for materials, specimens (fresh or dried), or books from the Library, will hand a requisition to Mr Tagg . . .

38. Statement of Accounts of the period. (In the RBG Library, Edinburgh).

39. Letter dated 13 February 1912 from Bayley Balfour to Sir Kenneth McKenzie, in the RBG Library, Edinburgh:

> Dear Sir Kenneth. In older times I used to find my personal touch with Spring Rice and Bergne at the Treasury of inestimable value in the furtherance of the Garden development. You will understand therefore that I fully appreciate the point of your letter and I shall not fail to comply with Mr Wilkin's wish on my next visit to London. In recent years when I have had no personal friends at the Treasury I should have been lost but for the sympathetic help you have been so good as to give me always, and I rather feel that so far as my Garden schemes are concerned my personal contact with Mr Wilkins may not be quite of the benefit that has accrued from your powerful advocacy. At the same time I am consoled by thinking that it may perhaps save you some of the trouble which I frequently impose upon you. Interpreting your reference to Mr Harrow's increase of salary as the shadow of a coming event I am happy and grateful to you. Our Librarian is in process of appointment. My own assistant is now in harness, and as you gave me also last year a plant propagator I should be ill to please did I not say that 'things are going well' and in saying this I do not forget how much I am indebted to you . . .

40. Bayley Balfour's contact with Stevenson was mainly but not exclusively, connected with research into the life and work of George Don, who was Principal Gardener at the Edinburgh Botanic Garden from 1802 to 1806. Their correspondence on the subject of Don and other matters is in the RBG Library, Edinburgh. Balfour was very much impressed by the proven qualities and abilities of Stevenson and believed that they would be ideal for the post of Librarian at the University College in Dundee for which Stevenson was an applicant, for a second time in twenty years. Stevenson, however, did not get the job. (See Appendix 6). As Stevenson himself perhaps knew, his age was against his chances.

41. FLETCHER, Harold Roy and BROWN, William Hunter (1970). *Royal Botanic Garden Edinburgh, 1670–1970*. Edinburgh, HMSO, p. 222.

42. These early Registers are in the RBG Library, Edinburgh.

43. At the time of typing-out the hand-written catalogue entries, many interesting, cited locations were encountered; that quoted in the text being just one of them. By 1984, there were still a few catalogue entries giving the location as 'Press', which in Scotland is commonly used for a cupboard.

Most of the typing was carried out by Betty Bee, who replaced Margaret Cormack as Library Typist in 1971, and continued in the post until February 1984 when she was transferred to the general typing pool.

44. *Trans. Proc. Bot. Soc. Edinburgh*, 1931, vol. 30, p. xxx.

45. *Ibidem*, 1948, vol. 34, p. xxii.

46. *Notes from the Royal Botanic Garden, Edinburgh*, 1939, vol. 20, no. 96, pp. 1–53.

47. Bayley Balfour's letter dated 10 May 1922 to William Wright Smith:

> . . . I agree in all you say about your staff—there is an atmosphere of keenness and willingness which is most gratifying and means efficiency.

In the same paragraph Balfour continued:

Beware the renewal of the attempt on the part of the University to 'pigeon-hole' duties of its Assistants. I think I discussed with you this fatal form of Trade's Unionism when it was first mooted. Nip any suggestion of it in the bud for your own comfort.

48. William Wright Smith's letter dated 22 April 1922 to Bayley Balfour:

I am just now in correspondence with the Board over the question of renewal of the Library grant. They first of all made me a reference asking how the odd £15 was explained and I have satisfied them on that point. They seem to have lost all their own papers dealing with the original sanction of that £15. Yesterday I had a further reference asking me to state afresh the case for the grant of £200 as again head quarters had mislaid all papers dealing with the subject. Search here failed to reveal any trace of the file which no doubt contained your original letters supporting the claim. As you were dealing with the question of the renewal of the grant towards the end of February it is just possible that you may have retained the papers. I have an impression that some years ago you showed me a statement by Sir William Thiselton-Dyer at the time when he was urging further financial support for the scientific library at Kew. I can of course if need be make out a case *de novo*, but I shall be very grateful if you can give me any reference to a file which could contain useful matter . . .

49. Bayley Balfour's letter dated 25 April 1922 to William Wright Smith. This letter, like all others mentioned here, is also in the RBG Library, Edinburgh. Balfour's handwriting is difficult to decipher in many places, but there is no mistaking his meaning.

50. Balfour's letter is in numbered paragraphs. The quotation is from para. 12. The last word is not clear.

51. The list of the contents of the four cases is in the file of Lady Balfour's letters at the RBG, Edinburgh. Letters in this file also refer to many other things, especially papers relating to the Library of the Garden and correspondence with some of the notable botanists and horticulturists of the day, which Lady Balfour sent to Smith in Edinburgh.

52. *Science and Art Department. Edinburgh Museum of Science and Art. List of books, etc., relating to Botany and Forestry, including the Cleghorn Memorial Library, in the Library of the Museum.* Edinburgh. Printed by Neill & Company for Her Majesty's Stationery Office, 1897.

53. The many donations from Cleghorn over several years to the Library of the Botanical Society of Edinburgh and to the Royal Botanic Garden Library are to be found in the lists of donations appearing in the early volumes of the *Transactions and Proceedings of the Botanical Society of Edinburgh* and also in the Garden's own reports. An obituary of Dr Cleghorn appeared in *Trans. Proc. Bot. Soc. Edinb.*, 1896, vol. 20, pp. 439–448.

54. *The Herbal Review,* 1978, vol. 4, no. 3, pp. 15–20.

55. The Society's library was auctioned by Sotheby's on 13 March 1967 (See Ref. 54 above, p. 16).

56. NOBLE, Mary (1961). Malcolm Wilson . . . In *Yearbook of the Royal Society of Edinburgh,* pp. 39–41.

57. All letters relating to this are in the RBG Library, Edinburgh.

58. *Proceedings of the Linnean Society of London,* 1963, vol. 174, p. 155.

59. *Trans. Bot. Soc. Edinb.* 1947–50, vol. 35, pp. 97–102, 109–119, 207–357. All these papers have additional plates.

60. *Taxon,* 1963, vol. 12, no. 3, pp. 89–102.

61. Librarian's Annual Report, 1964. RBG Library, Edinburgh.

62. See Chapter 3, Notes and References, No. 1.

63. FLETCHER, H R and BROWN, W H (1970). *Royal Botanic Garden, Edinburgh 1670–1970.* Edinburgh, HMSO.

64. Referring to Bayley Balfour's application for money for the Garden's educational

activities Sir S K McDonnell of HM Office of Works wrote privately to Balfour on 2 March 1906:

I had some conversation with MacLeod on Monday night, and I find that in principle he would not be averse to some money being allotted from the grant of the Scottish Education Department in order to provide accommodation for teaching purposes at the Gardens. I ought, however, to warn you that he was careful to safeguard himself by reminding me that he has no voice in the disposition of this money, it being a matter with which Mr Struthers is primarily concerned.

I do not know whether you are acquainted with Mr Struthers: if so I imagine that the best course would be for you to communicate privately and unofficially with him and see what his attitude is. It is rather a delicate matter to handle because, rightly or wrongly, the Scotch Education Department are thought to be desirous of acquiring the entire control of the Gardens: If this should ever come to pass it would mean a divided jurisdiction, for, we should be responsible for the buildings and they for everything else, and, judging from what I have seen at Kew under the new dispensation I should say that you would find such an arrangement the reverse of desirable.

I mention this because the Scotch Education Department may regard any movement on our part to get money from them as an implied admission of their interest in the Gardens: and complications may ensue.

Perhaps you will let me know what you think.

Balfour did not waste any time putting pen to paper expressing his thoughts on the matter. He wrote to McDonnell on 5 March 1906:

The numbing influence of dual control—of Treasury through the King's Remembrances and of the Office of Works—has already been felt here. Only after 1889 when control was centred in the Office of Works did I find progressive development possible, and so long as the Regius Keeper receives—as I have been fortunate in receiving—the sympathy and support of the Board the maintenance of the Garden as the headquarters of botanical education in Scotland is assured. I am not, therefore, as you may suppose, willing to do anything that may bring about the reimposition of a dual control with different factors, even though the new one should promise so much as does the Scottish Education Department.

I am conscious, however, that no argument against dual control would have much force in opposition to a declared desire of the Scottish Education Department to acquire entire educational control of the Garden. More forceful is the objection that the position of the University would be prejudiced by such a transfer. Although unfortunately the recommendation of the Treasury Committee of 1890 for the placing of the relationships between the Crown and the University in regard to the Garden on a definite footing have not yet been carried out the existing understanding—which, briefly stated, is in practice that the Crown furnishes equipment for teaching and the University provides Salary for Regius Keeper—is sufficient to give the University a paramount educational position in the Garden and this would be affected by the introduction of another educational body as the controlling power. Any proposal of the kind I am sure would provoke the hostility of the University and would raise complicated issues.

If the Scottish Educational Department has the desire which you say is attributed to it, it will sooner or later advance its claim to absorb the Garden. We should do nothing to hasten the moment of this, and I agree with you that any movement to get money from the Department for its prospective requirements would give it an opportunity. Even informal communication between myself and Mr Struthers should not take place I think in the circumstances, and we should await the initiation of the Scottish Education Department of negotiations for giving it what it needs.

This attitude of the Scottish Education Department seems to me however to add policy to the educational and other reasons I have placed before the Board in support of my plea of urgency for improved accommodation in the Garden. Our scheme of reconstruction of buildings which the Treasury deferred was as you know framed before possible requirements of the Scottish Education Department were on the horizon, and it provides for our present needs and those of the immediate future. We should be in a much stronger position to resist any attempt at absorption by the

Scottish Education Department were we able to offer it the use of the equipment we should possess under the scheme. May I hope therefore that the Committee to which you propose to refer our scheme will meet in course of the Summer in time sufficient to permit of the inclusion in the Estimates of next year of some provision for it?

I am most grateful to you for having spoken to Sir Reginald MacLeod and that you have been able to learn the probable intentions of the Scottish Education Department.

65. DAVIS, Peter H, HARPER, Peter C and HEDGE, Ian C (eds) (1971). *Plant life of South-West Asia*. Edinburgh. Botanical Society of Edinburgh.

66. HEDGE, I C and LAMOND, J M (eds) (1970). *Index of collectors in the Edinburgh Herbarium*. Edinburgh, HMSO.

7 The Libraries at Inverleith III, 1970-1984

DOUGLAS MACKAY HENDERSON

Douglas Mackay Henderson succeeded Fletcher as Regius Keeper in 1970. He had come to the Garden in 1951 when William Wright Smith was in charge. During Fletcher's later years Henderson assisted in the planning of the new Herbarium and Library Building and in the management and administration of the Garden. As he was also an enthusiastic Supervisor of the Library, his appointment as Regius Keeper was particularly encouraging to the Librarian.

The most outstanding development in the Library under Henderson was the remarkable growth of its stock of literature. Within 14 years of his taking office, by the end of 1984, library stock more than doubled in size. Several of the additions filled some of the long standing gaps in many sections of stock—early works, runs of journals, botanical illustrations, garden history, and not the least, archival materials.

Although their number varied from year to year, exchanges certainly brought in more journals and books, particularly from eastern European

21. Joachim Schliemann's book plate attached to Aubriet & Vaillant's Champignons et Plantes Fongueuses. *18×22.5 cm.*

countries, including the USSR,[1] and from China.[2] When financial difficulties threatened the publication of the *Transactions of the Botanical Society of Edinburgh,* Henderson arranged for the Garden to purchase from the Society the copies required for exchanges.[3] This was enlightened self-interest, reminiscent of Bayley Balfour's championship of the same publication in 1890. The publication of the Transactions was important because, without it, the Garden would have had to buy the journals and books received in exchange for it, and the amount involved would have been in excess of the money given towards its purchase.

Henderson's public relations led to a good deal of archival material being deposited in the Library. Among the items received are the minute books of the Royal Caledonian Horticultural Society, diaries, field books, letters and other papers of botanists, horticulturists and plant collectors such as John Ramsbottom, Charles McIntosh, Beatrix Potter,[4] George Forrest, Frank Ludlow and George Sherriff, and botanical paintings of Margaret Stone, and others.

Gifts and bequests, too, contributed to the growth of the Library. Particular mention is to be made in this regard of the gift of the library of the prominent Scottish horticulturist Robert Scarlett of Inveresk, in 1975. The library

22. Alfred Schmid's book plate attached to Aubriet & Vaillant's Champignons et Plantes Fongueuses. *13×11 cm.*

contained some 400 books, some of them scarce botanical and horticultural works, mostly of the late nineteenth and early twentieth centuries.

The last decade saw a marked increase in the number and quality of Library purchases. Several of the earlier works bought from the second-hand market in Britain and overseas, and at auctions, were important additions to the botanical literature collection, rarely seen elsewhere in Scotland. J Commelin, *Horti Medici Amstelodemensis rariorum . . .* 2 vols, (1697–1701); A P de Candolle, *Plantes rares du Jardin de Genève,* (1829, consolidated edition) folio; E M Fries, *Sveriges ätliga och giftiga Svampar* (1861); and S Vaillant, *Champignons et Plantes Fongueuses . . .* (ca. 1720) are just a few examples. The last mentioned is a unique work of some 500 original water-colour illustrations by Aubriet with Latin nomenclature by Vaillant[5] (Plate 3; Figs 21, 22). Among the later publications bought by the Library were: C Gesner, *Historia Plantarum . . .* 8 vols, folio (1972–1980; facsimile); E Malins, *Red books of Humphry Repton,* (1976); A George and C E Rosser, *The Banksias,* vol. 1 (1981); and J Rourke, *Mimetes . . .* (1982).

Scores of early works, beyond the resources of the Library to acquire in original printed form because of their rarity and expense, were bought in microform, as were some internationally known herbaria. Runs of journals, in their original form, were added to the periodical holdings, equally through purchase and gifts.

All these purchases needed money. Without the helpful attitude of the Department of Agriculture and Fisheries for Scotland the required finance would not have been available and the Library would have been so much poorer. Even at the height of severe cut-backs in library expenditure throughout the Civil Service in 1975–1976 the Library actually added to its current titles, limiting cuts to two journal subscriptions.[6]

Small libraries of books and journals were provided at the three satellite gardens at Benmore in Argyllshire, Logan near Stranraer in Wigtownshire and Dawyck in Peeblesshire, specifically for the use of staff in those gardens. Some current journals of particular interest to these staff were sent to them regularly.[7]

The unprecedented growth of library stock inevitably created a very acute problem of accommodation. In 1981 mobile shelving units were installed in the long library store to house the less frequently used runs of journals, thus releasing some space in the main Library for a little better keeping of the rest of the stock.

Soon after Henderson took office, the big Ericales Project was launched. The Garden had been known the world over for its collection of plants belonging to the order Ericales, particularly the genus *Rhododendron,* and the project was aimed at collecting, growing, studying and reporting on as many of these plants as possible.[8] At a staff meeting called to report on the progress of the project in 1972, Henderson announced that as part of the Library's contribution to the project a comprehensive, annotated bibliography of all post-Linnean literature of the Ericales would be compiled.[9] This was an enormous task for the Library to undertake. But it was an opportunity for the librarians to put to good use their training and expertise in the compilation of a large bibliography which could be a useful tool at the Garden and to many beyond. So the Librarian applied himself to the compilation with considerable enthusiasm. At the time his assistant was David Parker who had succeeded

Milne in February 1971. Neither Mathew nor Parker really had any spare time to engage in the new assignment. It was inevitable that the management and administration of the Library would suffer. But with the expected additional staff assistance these difficulties would be kept at reasonable levels.

Parker left in March 1975, and was replaced by Lynda Clark, almost fresh from library school. As the work situation in the Library was getting difficult, Mathew discussed the matter with James A Ratter, the Supervisor of the Library at the time. Eventually in 1976 there was a staff inspection of the Library carried out by the Scottish Office. The report recommended the appointment of an additional Clerical Assistant, and suggested that the Library should undertake more bibliographical work and also produce a library bulletin. Representations on the unacceptability of the staff inspection report were made to the Department. But the only concession it was prepared to make was the temporary appointment of an Assistant Librarian, Erica Baber, from September 1978 to July 1979. The Clerical Assistant was never appointed. In the meantime, the permanent assistant, Clark, had left on maternity leave in May 1979, and was to resign her post in February 1980. Once again there was no Assistant Librarian for over a year until August 1980 when Deborah Anne Morrison was appointed to the post, bringing staff strength to its level in 1966 when there was an intake of only 485 monographs and 796 serials as opposed to 992 monographs and 1411 serials in 1980.

The formation of the independent Edinburgh Botanic Garden Trust in October 1977 was the idea of Burtt. Though retired in 1975, he was still very actively engaged in botanical research and writing, and interested in the Garden Library. The object of the Trust, which became fully operational in 1978, was to help the Garden in matters that cannot be financed from Government funds. As far as the Library was concerned, the Trust would welcome gifts of books; those required by the Library would be presented in the name of the donor, the remainder would be sold for Trust funds. By 1984 the Library had received through the Trust several books, among them, some very useful additions to the Library's collection of early textbooks on botany: Christian Hendrik Persoon, *Synopsis Plantarum seu Enchiridium Botanicum . . .* (1805–1807); Edward Step, *Hardy Bulbous Plants, Florilegium Harlemense . . .* plates by A Goossens (1908); and Charles Darwin, *Variation of Animals and Plants under Domestication*, 2 vols (1868).

Another benefit the Library received from the Trust was financial help to pay for the sorting of the vast archival collection and arranging it in some useable fashion. It was James Burnett, formerly a member of the Garden's administrative staff, who did the work. As a result most of the Garden's archives were in a much better condition in 1984 than they had been for a very long time, although considerable work remained to be done to bring all archives together and make them useful for productive research.

In March 1983 the Secretary of the Department of Agriculture and Fisheries for Scotland announced that a Scientific Review Group was to be appointed later in the year to review the work of the Garden, as similar groups had done in 1970 and 1976. Following on the heels of that announcement, the staff of the Garden were officially informed of the intention of the Secretary of State for Scotland to separate the Garden from the main stream of Civil Service under the Scottish Office and hand over responsibility for its management and administration to a Board of Trustees. Public announcement of this came in

October 1983.[10] This impending change in the status of the Garden was not, however, a matter for the consideration of the Review Group[11] when they came in September. They looked at all departments of the Garden including the Library and interviewed all senior staff, and the Librarian. Their report, presented early in 1984, was confidential to the Secretary of the Department of the Scottish Office responsible for the Garden. One of the results of that report was a staff inspection of the Library in 1984. The two members of the Manpower Organisation of the Scottish Office who inspected the Library between June and September produced their report in late October.

Apart from reiterating the recommendation of the 1976 staff inspection report to appoint an additional Clerical Assistant, the only other offer the 1984 report contained was the appointment of a temporary Assistant Librarian to help clear all the backlog of work. The inspectors considered that the posts of librarians were correctly graded. In effect, numerically, staff strength was to remain at the 1966 level because just before the staff inspection the post of library typist had been removed from the Library, and the additional Clerical Assistant would be replacing that post.

On 12 November 1984 Andrew Grierson resigned his position of Library Supervisor. James Cullen, the Assistant Keeper, took up that position. On 20 December 1984 the Regius Keeper appointed the Librarian as Chairman of the Library Advisory Group, and asked him to join the RBG Management Group.

NOTES AND REFERENCES

1. Prof. Peter H Davis's *Flora of Turkey and the East Aegean Islands* is an essential work of reference to many botanists in the USSR and neighbouring countries. Monetary and other difficulties, however, prevent them from obtaining copies of the various volumes of the Flora. Henderson made it possible for the Garden Library to buy copies and send them to these colleagues who, in exchange, would send to Edinburgh a number of their publications in botany and horticulture.

2. The Garden has had a close relationship with China from Bayley Balfour's time, and there was a regular exchange of publications. During the long years of silence from China, successive Regius Keepers continued to send their publications to all whose addresses were on the mailing list. In recent years when China began to open its doors to the outside world, exchange publications began to arrive from old friends and institutions. By 1984 the Garden was exchanging publications with 14 botanical gardens and institutions in China.

3. The Botanical Society of Edinburgh used to give the Garden, free of charge, as many copies of their Transactions as were required for maintaining the exchange agreements. Latterly the Garden has contributed financially towards the production cost by purchasing the copies it requires for exchange purposes.

4. Dr Mary Noble, a long standing member of the Botanical Society of Edinburgh, and friend of the Garden, was responsible for the deposit of letters and other papers of Beatrix Potter, John Ramsbottom and Charles McIntosh, in the Library. She also obtained for the Library specific books from time to time, for example, William Cole's *The Art of Simpling* . . . London (1656).

5. Entry in A Asher & Co. (1983). *Books on Botany, Catalogue XXVIII*, p. 126:
'1102 (AUBRIET, C [&] S VAILLANT) *Champignons et Plantes Fongueuses.* (109.11., containing ca. 500 fine watercolour illustrations, drawn by Aubriet, with Latin nomenclature supplied in ink by Vaillant; mostly in a black ruled border). France, ca. 1720. Large folio. (47×35 cm). Contemporary calf-backed boards, spine gilt (worn) (now neatly repaired). Dfl. 37.000

Uellner, Bibl. Schliemann,(*) 37 (this volume). A fine group of watercolours by perhaps the greatest French botanical artist of the 18th century. Title from the strictly contemporary binding: 'Champi/et Plant/fongue/par Aubrie'. This attribution of authorship (the drawings are unsigned) is corroborated by their elegant and accurate style which are characteristic for the work of the 'peintre du Roi, au Jardin du Roi'. Collections of original drawings by Aubriet are preserved in various public institutions, a.o. in the Bibliotheque Nationale in Paris and in Gottingen University Library (see Nissen, BBI, pp. 98–100, suppl., p. 6); two watermarks in the paper of our volume are, according to Uellner, identical with those found in the paper of the Aubriet drawings in Gottingen. Aubriet participated in several projects together with the famous botanist Vaillant, to whom the legends in this collection are attributed; he designed the illustrations for Vaillant's Botanicon Parisiense (1727). The drawings are mounted (one is detached); occasional staining or browning. An attractive and uncommon collection in excellent condition with a good provenance: formerly belonging to the collection of Dr Alfred Schmid of Berne, and Joachim Schliemann, with their bookplates.

(*)UELLNER, Winfried, ed. Fungorum libri bibliothecae Joachim Schliemann. Vaduz, J Cramer, 1976.

6. The two journals cut were Planta and Chromosoma. They were really concerned with subjects outwith the immediate interests of the Garden. In any case, both of them were taken by the Botany Library of the University.

7. All three satellite gardens were sent some current journals, and other journals were sent to them in circulation. Dawyck had by 1984 only some 10 to 15 books. The other two had somewhat larger collections, particularly Benmore, which had a long run of the Journal of the Royal Horticultural Society (now The Garden).

8. Two important papers on the genus Rhododendron have been published: James Cullen (1980), Revision of Rhododendron, 1. Subgenus Rhododendron sections Rhododendron & Pogonanthum and David Chamberlain (1982), Revision of Rhododendron II. Subgenus Hymenanthes in Notes RBG Edinb., vol. 39(1) pp. 1–207 and vol. 39(2) pp. 209–486 respectively. Other papers on Ericaceous plants also have been published, such as those on Vaccinium by George Argent.

9. CULLEN, James (1984). Libraries and herbaria. In HEYWOOD, V H & MOORE, D M (eds), Current Concepts in Plant Taxonomy. London, Academic Press, p. 34 [Systematics Association Special Volume No. 25].

10. Scottish Office Press Notice, dated 11 October 1983.
Mr George Younger, MP, Secretary of State for Scotland, has decided to change the status of the Royal Botanic Garden and its 'satellite' gardens at Logan in Wigtownshire, Benmore in Argyll and Dawyck, Peeblesshire. Mr Younger is to seek legislation to establish the Garden—at present an integral part of the Scottish Office—as a separate body grant-aided by the Department of Agriculture and Fisheries for Scotland and managed by a Board of Trustees. The Secretary of State is confident that this change in status will provide the Royal Botanic Garden with the opportunity of a more flexible, autonomous and effective approach to its diverse and specialised areas of interest.

11. The members of the Scientific Review Group were: Prof. W W Fletcher (Chairman), Prof. C H Gimingham, Prof. J P M Brennan, Dr E J Balfour, Mr D C M Corbett, Mr C D Brickell, Dr D Martin, Dr T W Hegarty and Mr R B Wilson (Secretary).

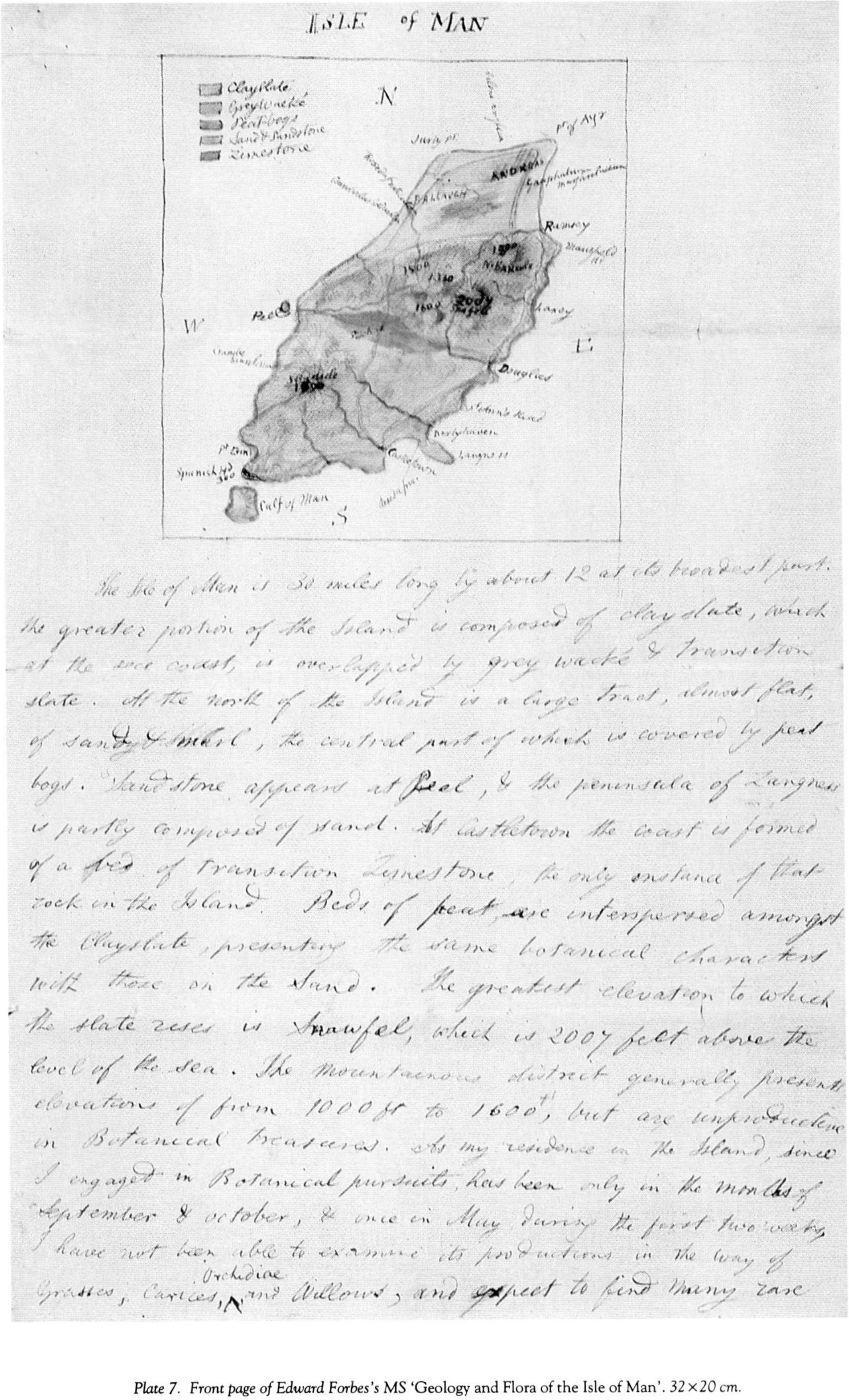

ISLE of MAN

The Isle of Man is 30 miles long by about 12 at its broadest part.
The greater portion of the Island is composed of clay slate, which
at the sea coast, is overlapped by grey wacké & transition
slate. At the north of the Island is a large tract, almost flat,
of sand & marl, the central part of which is covered by peat
bogs. Sandstone appears at Peel, & the peninsula of Langness
is partly composed of sand. At Castletown the coast is formed
of a bed of transition Limestone, the only instance of that
rock in the Island. Beds of peat, are interspersed amongst
the Clayslate, presenting the same botanical characters
with those on the Sand. The greatest elevation to which
the slate rises is Snawfel, which is 2007 feet above the
level of the sea. The mountainous district generally presents
elevations of from 1000 ft to 1600^{ft}, but are unproductive
in Botanical treasures. As my residence in the Island, since
I engaged in Botanical pursuits, has been only in the months of
September & October, & once in May during the first two weeks,
I have not been able to examine its productions in the way of
Grasses, Carices, Orchideæ, and Willows, and expect to find many rare

Plate 7. *Front page of Edward Forbes's MS 'Geology and Flora of the Isle of Man'. 32×20 cm.*

Plate 8. *One of the coloured drawings of the Scottish explorer Mungo Park.* 43.5×28.5 cm.

8 The Library at the end of 1984

At the close of 1984, as during much of its long life, the main function of the Royal Botanic Garden in Edinburgh is botanical and horticultural research with very particular emphasis on taxonomic research. The whole establishment—the Garden, Planthouses, Herbarium, Library, Laboratories, Studios—is geared for this. The public amenity the Garden provides, its educational activities, the exhibition hall and other departments, are other important aspects closely interrelated with the research activities.

On the staff of the Garden are botanists specialising in taxonomy, horticulturists, gardeners, librarians, photographers, graphic artists, exhibition officers, public relations officers, teachers, administrators and supporting staff at different levels. The purpose of the Library is to acquire, organise and disseminate relevant literature to all staff with special attention to the needs of taxonomic research.

Taxonomic botany, as has been noted earlier, leans heavily on history. Taxonomists, therefore, need to refer to literature of the past two or three hundred years just as much as they need to examine current publications. Naturally the Library provides a large number of early botanical works. This collection is added to from time to time when suitable items become available. Valuable early book collections in many libraries and elsewhere tend to be regarded as possessions to be treasured or as investments to be guarded. The Garden Library also prizes its collection of early works but they are considered more as regular working tools just as contemporary publications, and made available for use with little formality.

Botanical literature is truly international. It is published in practically every language in the world. This accounts for the high proportion of foreign language material in the Library. Latin, of course, remains the official international language of the taxonomist; the original diagnosis of a plant, if not the full description, has to be published in Latin if it is to be valid. Several early works were entirely in Latin.

A botanical library is apt to be large because of the vast volume of literature published in the field of botany and related subjects and the need for it to provide at least a fair part of that literature for its users. Scope for editing or weeding of stock is limited because the library is obliged to preserve its holdings for posterity, much as a national library. This accounts for the fast growth of the RBG Library. The Garden's history, the contribution of its earlier Regius Keepers towards the progress of botany and, above all, its close association with the Botanical Society of Edinburgh accelerated the growth of the RBG Library by bringing to the Garden not only a large number of publications, but a priceless collection of archival materials, including thousands of letters from botanists all over the world.

The growth of the Library was, until recently, largely through gifts and exchanges. One of the inevitable consequences of this was the unplanned expansion of stock, leaving many gaps in holdings, especially in earlier stock. Some of the items gifted were imperfect; those received in exchange were not always what were required. Not infrequently items received were duplicates or even triplicates of items already in stock, although, occasionally some of the books and other materials received turned out to be extremely rare and valuable.

Floras, botanical monographs, taxonomic revisions, bibliographies and bibliographical accounts, library catalogues, indexes, plant lists, language and subject glossaries and dictionaries, regular periodicals and abstracting and indexing journals, taxonomic works on cultivated plants, biographies, directories, colour charts, maps and gazetteers are some of the essential kinds of literature for the plant taxonomist. Some old and some new, all these appear as pamphlets, single or multi-volume works, complete in themselves or part of other works, professional or popular in style and treatment, illustrated or otherwise.

Those concerned with the maintenance of the Garden require literature on the culture of plants, soils, fertilizers, meteorology, plant pathology, ecology, pollution, conservation, garden design and history, economic plants, amenity horticulture and other materials of particular interest to them such as plant and seed lists from botanic gardens and nurserymen's catalogues. Subjects of interest to other professionals are graphic design and display, art and photography, education and teaching, leisure and recreation, editing and publishing, management and administration, library organization and information technology.

Books on physics, chemistry, natural science, particularly entomology and geology, land surveying, building construction, horticultural machinery and its maintenance, poisonous plants and chemicals, safety at work, law, town planning, landscape architecture, economics and many other subjects are of especial use for the students.

These are just some of the subjects in which the Garden Library is supplied with books and journals. It would be true to say that the Library holds the largest collection of botanical and horticultural literature in Britain, outside London (see p.129). Plant physiology, being only of peripheral interest to the Garden and catered for by the University Library, is not represented strongly in the Library. But, for historical reasons, there are good collections of early works on forestry and agriculture. Literature on early and contemporary medical botany is particularly well provided by herbals dating from 1486, pharmacopaeias, dispensatories, and other books and journals. There is also a large collection of botanical and horticultural drawings, prints, paintings and press clippings, not to mention the large archival collection, the fast growing microform collection including several old classics and some 15 internationally known herbaria such as those of Linnaeus, Boissier, Candolle, Lamarck, Reichenbach, Smith, Thunberg, Wallich, Willdenow and others, occupying some 75 linear ft. and the small number of audio-visual materials.

Of the volumes of stock in the Library about a third are books and the rest periodicals. The book stock is arranged in classified order according to a modified Bliss Bibliographical Classification system. The arrangement of the floras and taxonomic monographs corresponds to the arrangement of plant specimens in the Herbarium which is a definite advantage for the taxonomists searching for literature.

Periodicals are arranged alphabetically by title, mostly under the name of the country of origin.

The entire collection of pamphlets and separates are filed alphabetically by the name of the author. Except for the bound volumes of these, mostly of the last century, the rest are shelved in cardboard boxes for better and economic keeping and provide some measure of protection from dirt and dust.

The large collection of prints and clippings is mounted on boards and kept in vertical files, first in the alphabetical order of family names and then under each family, alphabetically by generic names, followed by specific names in similar order. This proves to be the best suited arrangement for the use of this collection by most people. Original paintings and other exceptionally valuable materials are kept separately in specially made boxes.

Maps and large atlases are filed in special flat cabinets, in close proximity to the other smaller atlases and collection of gazetteers and indexes to place names.

Much of the archival material is gathered in one place and kept in acid-free boxes. There is still a sizeable collection of letters and other materials especially those related to many plant-collecting expeditions of George Forrest in China and others elsewhere, which needs to be joined with the archival collection. Necessary staff and suitable accommodation are awaited to make this collection a more productive research resource.

The Library Catalogue on 4×6 in. cards is the key to the resources of the Library (see Table 1). It has three distinct parts: the Subject Index is an alphabetical list of all subject headings and sub-headings with their respective class marks under which library stock is arranged; the Classified Catalogue lists in classified order of subjects, the Library's holdings on particular subjects; the Author Catalogue is a chronological list of all publications held by the Library, under their authors' names in alphabetical order.

The catalogue uses a colour coding system to indicate the location of different items in the Library. Thus, all entries on white cards represent book stock filed in classified order on the book shelves; yellow entries are for pamphlets, separates and other smaller works filed in boxes at the back of the Library; early and rare book stock, kept in locked cases, is represented by blue entries; analytical entries for items selected from periodicals or elsewhere are on pink cards.

The catalogue has two special sections, kept separately. One is an Index to Monographs which lists, under an alphabetical order of generic names, all monographs appearing in journals or similar publications and not filed with monographs on the book shelves. The other section is a Biographical Index of references to botanists and others in related fields, noted mostly from periodical literature received in the Library.

Of the hundreds of analytical entries added every year to the catalogue and represented by pink entries, special mention may be made of the references to botanical gardens, herbaria and other research institutions and to accounts of botanical tours and collecting trips in various parts of the world.

The Ericales bibliography, mentioned in the previous chapter, is still being added to, although lack of staff impedes its progress. It includes some 4,000 references to *Rhododendron*; of the rest, a large number refer to *Vaccinium*.

Scientific and other professional staff of the establishment and students of the Garden's three-year horticultural course are the primary users of the Library. The members of the Botanical Society of Edinburgh have the right to use the Library for consultation. The Professor, staff and students of the Taxonomy Section of the University's Botany Department, with their rooms at the Garden, are regular users. Other University staff from Edinburgh and elsewhere also have free access. Students of Landscape Architecture, Art and others from educational and research institutions in Edinburgh use the Library particularly frequently when they are attending lectures at the Garden. There is a constant flow of botanists and horticulturists from Britain and abroad who require the use of the Library. Apart from all these there are the members of the public, representing a wide range of interests, visiting the Library regularly.

The Library functions as a self-service library. The system in operation for borrowing by garden staff and short and long-term visitors remains virtually the same as that adopted years before by Bayley Balfour. This causes difficulties in monitoring the loans and assessing the extent of the use made of the Library. Student loans are, however, separately recorded and controlled.

Although essentially a Reference Library, a limited number of inter-library loans are allowed, particularly to the University's class libraries and libraries of the Institute of Terrestrial Ecology and other institutions. Loans to other libraries are mainly through the lending services of the British Library and National Library of Scotland. The loans sent out by the Library far exceed those borrowed.

The level of library acquisitions has increased very considerably in recent years, more than doubling its stock in a little more than a decade. The expansion of the research activities of the Garden, its wider and deeper international involvement and co-operation in producing national floras of other countries, the increase in the number of botanical and horticultural publications, the awareness of the responsibility of Scotland's premier botanical establishment to acquire and make available at least a fair proportion of published literature in its areas of concern, and the acceptance of and support for all these by the Department of the Scottish Office responsible for the Garden contribute to this phenomenal growth. The stock of the Library at the end of 1984, more than in earlier years, justify its claim to be the National Botanical and Horticultural Library for Scotland.

The Library and its resources have been much overlooked in many bibliographic works. However, Hargreaves[1] mentioned the *Latin Herbarius* of 1485(?) (see pp. 29, 33); Bird[2] listed the Library's holdings of some 75 sixteenth century medical books, twenty of them not held anywhere else in Edinburgh; Stafleu and Cowan[3] cited the Library as location for a handful of books; Henrey[4] mentioned the Library only for items not seen elsewhere; and yet there were scores of books which should have been listed as being in the RBG Library, Edinburgh, if not for their botanical and horticultural interest, at least for their bibliographical rarity. To list all such would be far beyond the scope of this work. Copies of title pages and brief details of a very few are given in Appendix X.

NOTES AND REFERENCES

1. HARGREAVES, G D (Comp.) (1976). *A Catalogue of Medical Incunabula in Edinburgh Libraries*. Edinburgh, Royal Medical Society, no. 54.

2. BIRD, D T (Comp.) (1982). *A Catalogue of Sixteenth-century Medical Books in Edinburgh Libraries*. Edinburgh, Royal College of Physicians of Edinburgh.

3. STAFLEU, Frans A and COWAN, Richard S (1976– –). *Taxonomic Literature: a selective guide to botanical publications and collections* . . . Second edition. Utrecht, Bohn, Scheltema & Holkema. (By 1984 four volumes, covering author's names beginning with letters A-Sa. had been published).

4. HENREY, Blanche (1975). *British Botanical and Horticultural Literature before 1800* . . . 3 Vols. Oxford, University Press.

Appendix I

Documents relating to the compensation paid to Mrs Alston
for leaving her husband's plants in the Garden.

(Facsimiles of these documents are in the RBG Library, Edinburgh)

To the Right Honourable The Lords Commissioners of his Majestys Treasury

The Humble Petition of Mrs Alston Widow of the deceast Doctor Charles Alston late Professor of Botany &ct and Mrs Robina Alston his only child for their Behoof. and of Doctor John Hope Professor of Botany and Keeper of his Majestys Physick Garden in Scotland Sheweth.

That the said late Doctor Alston from an ardent Zeal to promote that Branch of Knowledge which was the peculiar object of his Profession did with great Labour and Expence make a very considerable Collection of Exotic Plants in his Maj's. Physick Garden at the Palace of Holyroodhouse and in order to rear and preserve the plants which require particular attention and assistance in this Climate. He was at a further and greater Expence in making some necessary alterations in the Garden in preparing and raising the Walls and Building a Green and Hott house all which consumed a very considerable part of the profits and Salary of his Office and he never had any allowance for these improvements or even for the necessary Repairs which alone must have amounted to a Considerable Sum of Money during his Incumbency which was no less than forty years.

That by these means your petitioners his widow and Daughter at his death found themselves in a much worse situation than they had reason to have Expected and were advised that they were entitled for their support to Carry off and Dispose of the Plants Roots &ct that had been purchased and raised by Doctor Alston, But were afterwards prevailed upon to allow them to Continue in the Garden till a Successor Should be appointed from whom they had a title to Demand them.

Doctor Hope who is now appointed Professor of Botany & Keeper of his Majestys Physick Garden has the satisfaction to Observe that the taste for that Branch of Knowledge is greatly increasing and has reason to flatter himself that in a Course of a few years he will be able to raise it to a Pitch beyond what it has hitherto ever been in this Country, But is sorry to observe also that the removal of these plants will be an invincible obstacle to that progress, as it is impossible to replace them either by Labour or money in very many years.

And farther that he and his Successors in office will have but little Encouragement to be at much Expense in augmenting with new Discovered Exotic Plants the Stock under their care. If Doctor Alston's heirs are not thought to deserve any allowance for the valuable and useful Improvements as well as necessary repairs made by him on the Garden.

May it therefore please your Lordships in consideration of the Premises To move his majesty to Grant Warrant to the Lord Chief Baron & other Barons of Exchequer in Scotland to make payment to the widow & Heir of Doctor Alston to the real value of the Plants purchased & Raised by him now in the Garden that the same may remain there in all time Coming for Such purpose as his Majesty shall think proper, as also to make a Suitable allowance to the Heir of the said Doctor Alston for the repairs and improvements made by him on the said Garden, as after proper inquiry made shall to the said Barons seem Sufficient. And your petitioner shall ever pray

Signed	Bethia Alston for self & Robina Alston
	26 Nov. 1761
Signed	John Hope

The Lord Commissioners of the Treasury duly passed on the petition to the Barons of Exchequer in Edinburgh, asking for their report:

My Lords

The Lords Commissioners of his Majestys Treasury having persued the enclosed Petition of Mrs Alston and others Command me to transmitt the same to you, and to desire your Lordships will report in what manner the Physick Garden at Holyroodhouse hath been kept up; whether at the Charge of the Crown or intirely out of the salary allowed to the Keeper of the said Garden, and also your opinion what is fit to be done in the matter of the said Petition.

I am
My Lords
Your Lordships
Most Humble Servant
Signed   Saml. Martin

Treasury Chambers
2d December 1761

And the Baron's reply was:

To the Right Honourable the Lords
Commissioners of his Majestys
Treasury

May it please your Lordships

In obedience to your Lordships Commands Signified to us by Mr Martin directing us to report in what manner the Physick Garden at the Holyroodhouse hath been kept up, whether at the Charge of the Crown or intirely out of the Salary allowed to the Keeper of the said Garden, and also to report our opinion what is fit to be done in the matter of a petition of Mrs Alston and others preferring to your Lordships and herewith transmitted; We have Enquired into the matter thereby directed and find that the Physick Garden has been kept up intirely by the Keeper, and it doth not appear that the Crown hath been at any Charge towards keeping up the same.

We have also Considered what is fit to be done in the matter of the said Petition and are humbly of opinion that the sum of One hundred and fifty pounds should be paid to the petitioner Mrs Alston for the use of herself and Daughter for and in consideration on the Expense her Husband was at the making necessary alterations and repairs and Building a Greenhouse and Hothouse in the said Garden and in Collecting Exotic and other plants Trees and roots proper for Lectures upon Botany, and leaving them in the said Garden, and we are also of opinion that the said Plants Trees and roots now in the said Garden are necessary for the continuance of Such Lectures and Could not be renewed without a much more Considerable Expence.

And we think it necessary further to acquaint your Lordships that in making the said enquiries it appears to us that in the year 1646 a Grant was made by King Charles the first to James Duke of Hamilton and his Heirs of Entail of the office of Hereditary Keepers of the Palace of Holyroodhouse, with all the Gardens Orchards and Bowling Greens thereto belonging, and whole Privileges Trees and Casualties pertaining to the same, and this Grant gives power to the said Duke and his Heirs of Entail of appointing under keepers one or more of the said Palace and Gardens and of appointing Gardeners & other servants for cultivating and keeping up the north and south Gardens, which north Garden is the Physick Garden in the petition mentioned.

That their Majestys King William and Queen Mary Granted a Charter to William and Ann Duke and Dutchess of Hamilton reeiling the former Grants to their predecessors of the Hereditary Office of Keeping and the said Palace and Gardens and of a park adjacent to the same with power to them to Possess the same and appoint Deputies, Gardeners and other servants, and in pursuance of the said Grants Ann Dutchess of Hamilton on the 2d of March 1716 appointed Doctor Alston the Petitioners Husband Keeper Depute of the said north of Physick Garden during her pleasure with power to him to do everything for the

Improvement of Botany as Mr James Sutherland and Mr. John Murray* and Doctor William Arthur her former keeper Depute did or might have done and after the Demise of the said Dutchess, the Duke of Hamilton renewed Doctor Alstons appointment and Granted the same during the Doctors life. and upon enquiry made by us of the Guardians of the present Duke of Hamilton concerning his Grace's Right in or to the said Physick Garden We are authorised to Inform your Lordships that they are willing, that the same should be enjoyed by the Professor of Botany under the said Duke during his Infancy in the same manner it was enjoyed by the former Professors under his ancestors and to do anything in their power for the purpose, all which is humbly submitted to your Lordships Great Wisdom by

		Your Lordships
		Most faithful humble servants
Edinburgh	Signed	Robt. Ord
Excheq. Chambers		Jo Maule
the 23rd February		John Grant
1762		Will Mure

The Lords Commissioners of the Treasury accepted the report of the Barons and wrote:

My Lords

The Lords Commissioners of his Majestys Treasury have considered your report on the Petition of Mrs Alston and others. Desire your Lordships will Cause Signature to be prepared and Transmitted hither for issuing out of any fund that you shall think proper, to the said Mrs Alston the sum of One hundred and fifty Pounds for the uses and Services in your Said report Mentioned. I am

		Mr Lords
		Your Lordships most faithful
Treasury Chambers		humble servant
11th March 1762	Signed	Saml. Martin

The Barons in Edinburgh obliged.

May it please your Lordships

In obedience to your Lordships Commands signified to us by Mr Martin the 11th of this month, directing us to prepare and transmit a Signature for Granting to Mrs Alston the sum of One Hundred and fifty pounds for the uses and services mentioned in our Report upon the Petition of the said Mrs Alston and others; We have prepared and herewith Transmit the same accordingly. and We have the Honour to be

		Your Lordships
		Most faithful humble
		servants
	Signed	Jo Maule
Edin. Excheq Chambers		John Grant
17 March 1762		Will Mure

---

*He is not mentioned in Fletcher and Brown's published history of the Garden. Possibly he looked after the Garden in Sutherland's declining years and stood in for Arthur who fled to Italy, leaving the garden unattended till Alston was appointed? This is supported by an earlier letter, dated 25 July 1745, [Scottish Record Office, GD 253/143/9/9] in which Alston refers to 'Mr Murray one of my predecessors . . .'.

Appendix II

Botanical professorship—press comment, 1820

The recent appointment of a Professor of Botany in the University is one of the grossest insults ever offered to the public. Not that we mean to find any fault either with the talents or acquirements of Dr Graham. Our objection would have equally applied, though the appointment had been given to Sir James Edward Smith. They have nothing to do with the character of the new Professor, but refer entirely to the conduct of those by whom he had been nominated. The circumstances of the Crown having the power to appoint the Keeper of the Botanical Garden from which the Professorship could not be advantageously separated, really enables Ministers to dispose of the Chair in the University. Now, it is a fact, that Dr Graham's appointment, as Keeper of the Botanical Garden, was *gazetted within a fortnight of the death of his predecessor*, and that ministers did not even deign to communicate their intentions to the Magisters! It is not, however, of the studied insult thus offered to our civic rulers, but of the injury that this precipitate filling up of one of the most lucrative and important professorships has occasioned to the interest of science, that we complain. A story is, we know, industrially circulated, that ministers offered the appointment in their gift to Mr Brown, who declined their acceptance. But, admitting this statement to be well-founded, it will not exculpate them from the charge of having abused their patronage. Why should the refusal of Mr Brown shut the door against every other applicant with the exception of Dr Graham? The botanical science of the Empire is not monopolised by *two* individuals. And if scientific merit, and not the influence of a Noble Duke, had really regulated the decision of Ministers, why should they not have waited till it was ascertained from the opinion of those entitled to judge on such a subject, whether the claims of Sir James Edward Smith, Dr Thomson, &c. were inferior to the claims of the other candidate? This was the only proper method of proceeding; but it is not difficult to discern why it was departed from. Had Ministers delayed Dr Graham's nomination, recommendations in favour of other candidates, who have not yet to earn a name in the scientific world, would have been presented, and it might then have been rather difficult for them to forward the views of the *protege* of their noble friend. It was certainly better to make the appointment without any competition, than in defiance of it. (*The Scotsman*, 8 January 1820, p. 13).

Appendix III

*Observations by the Regius Keeper of the Royal Botanic Garden
in Edinburgh, upon the proposed transfer of
the Royal Botanic Garden in Edinburgh to the University of Edinburgh,
under Clauses 20, 21, 22, 24 and 26 of the Universities (Scotland) Bill, 1888*

The transfer of the Royal Botanic Garden, as proposed in the Bill, would be, in the opinion of the Regius Keeper, inexpedient and impolitic, because—

1. *There is a practical difficulty in the transference.* The Royal Botanic Garden, with the adjoining Arboretum, receives an Annual Grant of about £4000. (in the Estimates 1888–89 the exact sum is £4155.). It is proposed to transfer the Royal Botanic Garden only, the Arboretum is not mentioned in the Bill; and if the transference be effected, the Arboretum would still have to be maintained by the State, about a fourth of the present Annual Grant being required for it. The result of this would be that on one side of a dividing wall the Crown would be responsible for the Arboretum, whilst on the other side the University would control the Royal Botanic Garden. Such an arrangement would not conduce to economy, and might lead to a considerable amount of trouble. It may be urged that this is no more than an argument for the transfer of the Arboretum also to the University; but this transference would involve a breach of the contract between the Crown, the City of Edinburgh, and the Fettes Trustees made in 1877 when the City purchased the Arboretum Grounds.

2. *The transference would be injurious to the Garden itself, and fatal to its continuance and development as a place of enjoyment and as a centre of national scientific education.* The maintenance charge would be a heavy one upon the revenue of the University, which, with every desire to maintain the Garden adequately, would find the burden too great for its resources. Buildings or plants are all more or less temporary, and require constant patching and renewing, and the capital expenditure necessary for rebuilding houses could hardly be borne by the University. The tendency assuredly would be to curtail expenditure in those parts provided for the enjoyment of the public, and to limit outlay to what might appear needful for teaching of University Students. The character of the Garden as a place of public enjoyment would thus inevitably suffer.

In its teaching functions, at the present time the Garden does not provide for University Students alone, but the general public and students from other institutions have access, and make use of it for scientific study; and specimens are freely supplied for educational purposes. Now, should it be placed under the University, this open character of the Garden would be destroyed. Every Student would have to matriculate before enjoying the privilege of the use of the Garden for study; for it is not likely that the University could give up its right to a matriculation-fee in the case of Botany alone of the subjects taught in it. Although, too, the University would certainly be liberal in furnishing specimens to other institutions, economy would limit the number produced and available for such purpose. The usefulness of the Garden would of necessity be restricted, and it would tend to lose its character as an institution open to every one, and to become one limited to matriculated Students of the University.

With regard to the future development of the Garden, it cannot be doubted that transference means arrest. In the suggestions for a Forestry School in Scotland which have been urged in public, the Royal Botanic Garden in Edinburgh is considered the centre, around which such a school could best be built up; and further, the Garden should be in Scotland what Kew is in England—a training and teaching ground for young gardeners. These are possibilities of development, and there are others, which, under the University, would be difficult, if not impossible, owing to the want of funds and the limitations to which reference has already been made.

3. *The transference would be injurious to the University itself, which has objected to it, and urged that the responsibility should not be thrust upon it.* The Garden has, as has been already said, other duties besides those connected with the University, which has not exclusive claim

upon it, nor any control over its affairs. The relationship of the University to the Garden is that its Professor of Botany has hitherto received from the Crown the Keepership of the Garden, and the University Students are thus able to attend his lectures in the Garden each one paying a fee to the Curator for the privilege, as does everyone who is not a University Student. But if the transference should be carried out, the University would have responsibilities outside its own proper sphere. Besides having to provide for the education of its Students, it would also be bound to cater for the enjoyment of the public, and this is a function without precedent. The tax upon its revenue would, however, be so heavy, that, notwithstanding the desire it would no doubt feel to maintain adequately the Garden, it would fail in the attempt, and in so doing lay itself open to the reproach of people for what they would certainly consider a neglect of duty. It would be a serious thing to create such a possible position for a University. It would be reversal of the policy hitherto followed by the State to hand over a National institution to the control of a body whose sphere of activity is limited. In the case of the Natural History Collection of the University of Edinburgh, Government took them out of the care of the University to place them in the Museum of Science and Art, that they might be better kept up and made more accessible to the public. The proposal in the Bill to transfer the Botanic Garden, if carried out, would have an opposite effect; it would mean less efficient maintenance, and possible restriction of access.

4. *On the grounds of public policy the transference appears open to question.* The State has hitherto maintained Botanic Gardens at Kew, Edinburgh and Dublin. Now it is proposed to rid the State of the responsibility for Scotland whilst it is retained for England and Ireland. It may be fairly asked, is the proposal a just one? Surely Scotland is entitled to have for herself what is not denied to sister kingdoms.

The proposal to transfer the Royal Botanic Garden to the University of Edinburgh is not an integral part of the Bill, and could easily be dropped out of it. Its inclusion may perhaps be traced to a mistaken idea of connection between the Garden and the University, due to the Establishment Grant for the Garden being voted with the monies for the Universities in Scotland. The vote for the maintenance of the Garden is included in that for the Royal Parks and Pleasure Grounds, and it is with these that the Royal Botanic Garden and Arboretum should be in future classed, receiving the whole annual grant in one sum, and being subject to the provisions laid down by Act of Parliament for them, and under which Kew Gardens are managed. Under such conditions it would be possible to remove the wall which now separates the Arboretum from the Botanic Garden, and thus throwing the two into one give to the public the great advantage of as free access to the Botanic Garden as they now enjoy to the Arboretum, and allow the Administration to lay out the whole ground under its care upon one satisfactory plan. Such a fusion, it is evident, could not take place if the Botanic Garden be transferred to the University.

The Regius Keeper of the Royal Botanic Garden would direct attention to the above considerations, which in his opinion, are sufficient to render expedient the withdrawal from the Bill of the Clauses providing for the transference of the Garden to the University of Edinburgh. .

Royal Botanic Garden,
April 1888

These Observations, printed and widely circulated, were based on Balfour's Inaugural Address on 1 May 1888, as Regius Professor of Botany in the University of Edinburgh and Regius Keeper of the Royal Botanic Garden, Edinburgh. The Address gave more facts and figures than in the Observations. A printed extract of the part of the Address relating to the subject is in the RBG Library, Edinburgh.

Appendix IV

Letter dated 28 October 1888 from Sir W T Thiselton-Dyer,
Director of Kew Gardens, to
the Secretary of the Board of Works and Public Buildings
defending his case for the maintenance of
a botanical library at Kew.

Subject. With reference to B.6804/88

Secretary,

I quite agree with the Treasury in their contention that, looking at the resources of the public libraries at Bloomsbury and South Kensington, there would be no justification for providing at Kew another library for either casual public reference, educational study, or library work. But the Kew Library has never lent itself to any of these purposes. It is a purely technical library the contents of which are specially confined to the subject matter of the establishment, i.e., the study and illustration of the contents of the garden, herbarium and museum. It has always been our aim to restrain the growth of the library as far as possible in order to keep down administrative expense. We therefore never dream of buying merely popular books or text-books, or indeed any of that class of scientific literature which ordinary public readers would be likely to expect to find in a library to which they had access.

Kew is however becoming more and more the most important centre of all these branches of research which relate to the classification and economic uses of plants for the whole world. If the collections maintained at Kew are to have any value at all they must be kept posted up to the present state of scientific knowledge. This is an arduous and incessant branch of the current duties of the scientific staff and it is only by self-sacrificing and persistent attention to it that the reputation of Kew as a scientific establishment has been lifted into its present eminence.

We should require then a copious and complete scientific library (within, of course, certain defined and rather narrow limits) even if it were confined to purely official use. And the Treasury should obviously not measure the use of the word official by the needs of every ordinary Government office. But of course it would be absurd to restrict the use of the scientific resources of Kew to the members of the staff. They are equally open to all properly qualified persons who wish to use them for purely scientific research. Such research requires that the person engaged in it should have in addition to the specimens the literature relating to them at his side. To say that the specimens shall be at Kew and the books at Bloomsbury or South Kensington is to place an insuperable bar upon the whole thing.

Perhaps an illustration may make the matter even clearer. The collections made by travellers cannot be named on the spot. The very object of such an establishment as Kew is to compare such collections and identify them. But how can we do this if we have not the 'books in which they may have been described. We might of course from our own scientific knowledge approximately classify them and put them away in their proper place in the herbarium. But then we should cease to be in touch with botanical work elsewhere. And now suppose a botanist comes to Kew who wishes to study the plants which yield guttapercha.

We place before him what we believe to be specimens of them. But he points out 'This is useless to me unless you can also place before me the works of the Dutch botanists (the plant being preeminently native to the Dutch East Indies) in which the plants are discoursed, described and furnished with names.' If we reply 'Oh you must go to Bloomsbury for that' he would think we were wilfully trifling with him and would probably set some one in Parliament to complain on our estimates, that we failed to give the information on which the public had a right to expect from us. The Bd will but think I am drawing on my imagination. What I am describing does actually happen. Hardly a week passes without some deficiency in our library being pointed out to us by some outside worker, who finds the use he or she wishes to make of the herbarium impeded for want of it.

Our great difficulty is not so much the supply of current isolated works connected with systematic and economic botany but the great increase of foreign periodicals in which plants are described. This is a great burden in many ways. But it is a fragment of the general intellectual development of the world and it will go on whether Kew keeps pace with it or not. I know no method by which an arbitrary limit can be assigned to the progress of scientific knowledge. Kew has been too long committed to a definite field of work to stop now unless it stops altogether and the Treasury will, on looking into the matter, find it impossible to say that along any given line 'Thus far shalt thou go and no further.'

(Sgd.) W.T.T.D.
28.10.[18]88

Appendix V

Letter dated 27 December 1890 from Bayley Balfour
to the President of the Botanical Society of Edinburgh.

My Dear President,

At the meeting of the Council of the Botanical Society held before the November meeting of the Society this year I brought forward, as you are aware, for consideration a suggestion that the Society should make a new departure, or rather, I should say, revert to a former practice and publish monthly accounts of its Proceedings, in which would appear short papers, accounts of discussions, notices upon vegetation, etc., many of which are of great interest and have a stimulating effect when published at once, but which lose their effect, and indeed are often never published at all, when held over as they are under existing arrangements—to be brought out in one part along with the Transactions of the Society. In the early days of the Society proceedings were, as you know, published monthly in one of the scientific journals, and much of the information contained in these notices is of great interest. At the present time our Proceedings are hardly worthy of the name—little more than is found on the billet of meetings being recorded—and this character of our Proceedings is, I consider, symptomatic of want of energy on our part, and of an incipient decadence which we know is apt to set in all societies after they have pursued for a time a successful career, unless the members bestir themselves and give renewed vigour to the Society.

The Proceedings of a Society surely betoken its doings, and judged by them as they are issued by ourselves. I am sure the most enthusiastic of our members could not but feel that the Society is in a somewhat lethargic condition. Our Treasurer moans over a diminishing reserve! Why should this be? Not because of lessening in Edinburgh of the members of those who are interested in botanical affairs, but, I believe, we have got into a groove in which we are slackening effort, and I am convinced we must make some endeavour and go along more vigorously than heretofore.

Now, what I have just said has a very direct bearing upon the proposal I made to the Council in November. I believe that the best evidence of our activity we could give would be the reinauguration of a monthly issue of our Proceedings. In making this proposal I did so in, as I regard them, the best interests of the Society as well as the interest of the science the society does so much to promote. In these days when priority is determined by date of publication it is a very great matter that publications of Societies should not be long delayed. The recognised issue by the Botanical Society of its monthly Proceedings would, I conceive, lead to our receiving papers for rapid issue which would otherwise go elsewhere. This is indeed no mere supposition on my part. I know at present of papers which will only come to the Society in the event of some rapid means of publication being adopted, and it is evident to think that if a worker knows the Society will bring out quickly the result of his work he is the more likely to become a member of the Society. It is no argument to resist the proposal I make to urge that if the Society's Transactions as published now were promptly brought out at the end of a session the requirements of all workers would be met. It is quite clear that a paper read at the first meeting of a session in November could not under existing arrangements be brought out for nine or ten months, i.e., at the end of July when the session closes.

At the meeting of Council in November, when I brought forwards my proposal, three criticisms (I cannot call them objections) were passed in the short conversation that followed the submission of my proposal, and I desire to refer to them.

1. I was asked would there be material enough for a monthly issue? Certainly there would not be if the Proceedings were no more than have appeared in recent publications of the Society. But I take it that the fact of there being this monthly issue would give the stimulus to make our Proceedings more interesting, and there can be no doubt that many papers now included in the Transactions of the Society would much more conveniently come into the Proceedings and many short notes which are communicated to the Society, but do not appear at all in the publications, would find a place in the monthly Proceedings. There would be material enough I have no doubt at all.

2. It was suggested that a number of matters which would issue from the Botanic Garden might be published by the Stationery Office for the Garden. Certainly, they might be so—but I think the suggestion of such a course most unfortunate. I do not need to point out the intimate connection there has always been between the Society and the Garden, and everyone would, I am sure, deprecate any step that might in the smallest degree produce a tendency to separation. The Garden has benefitted by the Society, and the Society has benefitted by the Garden—any procedure that led to separate publication of results of work done in the Garden would unquestionably tend to injure the Society, and in so doing would injure the Garden itself. The publications of the Society go a long way to bringing of exchange books to the Garden Library, and it is therefore clearly on that ground alone if on no other, the interest of those charged with the maintenance of the Garden to keep a jealous watch over the publication of the Society, to endeavour to support these, and to make them as available as possible. It would be suicidal in the present circumstances to bring out a Garden Bulletin which would be practically a rival of the publication of the Society.

3. The third point raised referred to finance. Can the funds of the Society bear the expense of the monthly issue? It was suggested that until the volume of Transactions now preparing is issued no step should be taken in connection with the proposed monthly issue of Proceedings. When the question of expense is fully examined it will be seen that after all a comparatively small additional expenditure can be considered to be involved in my proposal. Everyone will agree with me, I am sure, in saying that if we are to issue publications at all, they ought to be as good and as valuable as possible. Now our present issue of proceedings is altogether unsatisfactory, and even if we do not amend our ways and bring out a monthly issue of these, I would propose that we should amend our Proceedings as far as to make them more detailed and more descriptive of what is actually done by the Society. I would put it then that whether appearing in monthly issue or under our present system our Proceedings should be equally full and the same amount of printing should be involved whichever plan is followed. There would be no title pages in the monthly issue—or covers—to add to expense—perhaps occasionally a small portion of a page might not be covered in a monthly issue, but I question if the printing of a monthly issue would be appreciably more expensive than that of a printing proceedings in the way now adopted. The only expense to be incurred would be that of postage to members. I estimate that at the outside, the issue of any number to all members entitled to receive publications would cost 8/- which would mean an annual expenditure of between £4. and £5. on postage. This would not however be entirely additional to postage expenditure at the present time, for of course the Transactions in volume at the end of the session would be less bulky, and would therefore cost less in transmission. Whether the Society should or should not incur such expenditure is a question of consideration. For myself I have only one answer, that it would be a most wise procedure if the Society were to do so.

No other criticism was, I think, passed at the Council meeting of November upon the proposal I made, and in writing to you now, Mr President, and converting to this matter I do so in order to prepare you for the raising of the question at the Council meeting which will next take place, at which I propose to press my proposal for decision upon it by the Council. The terms of my proposal are these—I put it in the form of a motion:—

> The Council being of opinion that it is expedient that the Proceedings of the Society should be recorded in a more elaborate and more detailed manner than has been of late customary, and that the object for which the Society exists would be promoted were such Proceedings issued at intervals throughout the session, as thereby facilities for more rapid publication of results of botanical research would be provided, resolved and recommends to the Society—
>
> That the Secretary be instructed to draw up a full report of Proceedings of each meeting of the Society in which shall be incorporated short papers and notes, lists of donations etc., and that the Proceedings so prepared is issued monthly to members as a separate publication of the Society.

I shall then ask the Council to deliberate upon this, and I hope full consideration to all sides of the question will be given. After all, I only ask that the custom in force so late as session 1880–81, with regard to the publications of Proceedings, should be reinstituted, and that the custom of yet earlier years with regard to monthly issue should be reintroduced. I ought to have written this letter at a longer interval from the date of the meeting of Council, but it has come upon me unawares, being exceptionally early. I would, however, like to suggest that it might be well to ask the Secretary to call the attention of members of Council to the fact that this matter will come up for decision, and that it is important therefore that the full meeting should be held.

The point to be decided is one which I regard as critical and it demands well weighed consideration. The Botanical Society of Edinburgh still remains the only purely Botanical Society in Great Britain, after a successful career of over fifty years, and it behoves us to whom its destiny is entrusted to judge carefully the measures that we may adopt for the maintenance of its usefulness and of its prestige—and for the increasing of these if possible. It is because I think—am convinced indeed—that a change such as I propose is required, is imperatively called for by the circumstances of our day that I have ventured to bring it before the Council, and I believe that its adoption would bring great benefit to the Society.

I am, My dear President,
Yours faithfully.
(signed) Isaac Bayley Balfour.

Appendix VI

*Letters, etc., relating to the appointment of Librarian
to the University College, Dundee and
Bayley Balfour's recommendation of Alex P Stevenson for the Post.*

To the Council, University College, Dundee.

New Inn Entry
Dundee, 5th July 1909

Gentlemen,
I beg to offer myself for the post of Librarian to University College. I have been for over thirty years a partner in the firm of A & J Stevenson, Bookbinders, Dundee. My occupation has made me familiar with the handling and care of books. A lover of books all my days, I have a knowledge of their range and contents which might be of service to students and others. My character and general intelligence is known to many of the professors of the College; in particular I may refer you to Professor Steggall, Professor D'Arcy Thompson, and Professor Geddes, with all of whom I have had much intercourse as student, tradesman and friend. Professor I Bayley Balfour, Edinburgh, has kindly sent me the letter which I append.

Twenty years ago your Council did me the honour to select me as one of the two candidates between whom they voted finally in selecting the Secretary of the College. In the nature of things I cannot hope to give the length of service I might then have given, but my friends will testify to my activity, and my interest in the College, which has done much to make and mould me, has not diminished. In this interval too, I have been adding, I hope, to stores of knowledge which ought to make me more helpful in the post for which I am applying. Should you think me worthy of appointment, I shall not fail to do my best to justify your trust.

Faithfully yours,
Alex P Stevenson.

Copy of letter from Professor I Bayley Balfour, MD, FRS, Regius Professor of Botany, Edinburgh.

Royal Botanic Garden, Edinburgh
19 June 1909

Dear Mr Stevenson,
Our friendship, now dating from some years back, began through your enthusiasm in the matter of the life, work and writings of Scientific men of the past, which prompted you to write to me spontaneously and to give me immediate help and to offer more, in connection with a historical investigation upon which I was engaged. Since then our meetings have given me opportunities of benefiting by your erudition, of seeing your intense devotion to books, and of learning that your instinct as a bibliophile is guided by a sound critical judgment. As a Librarian of a good Library such as that of the University College, Dundee, you would be in your element and the Library would have in you an Official in whom are associated those qualities of trustworthiness, accuracy of method, diligence in work and research, facile literary expression, and untiring willingness to help others, which go to the good merit even of a Library itself and to the rendering of it available to others who wish to use it.

I wish you all success in your application for the post, and hoping to hear that you have been successful.

I am,
Yours truly,
Isaac Bayley Balfour.

Newspaper cutting:

New librarian of Dundee University College

The new librarian of Dundee University College is Mr James A S Barrett, MA, FSA, Scot., Edinburgh. There were 34 applicants for the post, and a short leet of three was drawn up. The final selection was made yesterday by the College Council. The new librarian was educated at Edinburgh Academy and at the University of Edinburgh, where he graduated MA in 1894. In the following year he turned his attention to library work, and in the Edinburgh Public Library he became acquainted with the routine of lending and reference departments and with all details of library management. He has compiled a catalogue of the Edinburgh University Library, and in 1900 edited the biographical section of Harmsworth's Encyclopaedia, published by Messrs Nelson & Sons, Edinburgh. In 1902 he was appointed out of 149 applicants to the post of sub-librarian in the London Library, and for three months he had entire charge of all departments of the library. Mr Barrett has also considerable experience in library work, and in reading the proofs of work of a technical nature. He was on the short leet for the librarianship of Sheffield University, and more recently for that of the Royal College of Physicians, Edinburgh.

Appendix VII

Recollections of Mrs E[velyn] Betty V[eronica] Fletcher (née Sloan)
who was Johnstone's assistant from 1937 to 1942.

My salary was £3. less insurance 2s. 9d. No leave was allowed until I had worked for one year. Three special days leave and two privilege leave days were allowed and these were added on to two weeks holiday per year.

Johnstone was friendly and helpful. He was small in stature because of very stout legs, sallow in complexion with greying hair and a short, grey military moustache, but his brown twinkling eyes shone through gold-rimmed spectacles. His hobbies were gardening and bridge. A great lover of books, the handling of them gave him much pleasure; he was docile in character, but could be stubborn in argument. Trained as a mathematician, he was precise and punctual in habits, methodical in practice.

He took the train every day from Blackhall to Granton Road Station, walked to the Garden, brought lunch with him which he ate in a corner of the Library, always finishing with a James Grieve apple of his own growing as long as stock lasted. His visits to the dentist, like his periods of leave were twice yearly: in April a week in Aberdour and in August two weeks in Whitby. But when he reached his maximum salary (I think £800. per annum) he changed the two summer weeks from Whitby to Torquay, spending a night each way in London with a cousin in Westminster. He was ideally and happily married for many years to Maggie, but they had no children.

He had a curiously inquisitive side to him as well. I recall Dr Marie Campbell (later married to Dr Roger Waterston of the Royal Scottish Museum) arriving in the Library in an exquisite new black coat all the rage that particular season (I had one too!) and Mr Johnstone going up to her and enquiring if 'she was dressed in mournings'. Also, when I was expecting my first child, he said one day 'either your overall has shrunk in the wash or you are becoming very stout'. So I had to tell him my secret!

The Library was open daily from 9am to 5pm and on Saturdays from 9am to 1pm. On Thursday evenings from 7 to 9pm the Library was open for the Student Gardeners, at that time called Probationers. Each day at 11am the Professor, Sir William, came to the Laboratory to have tea with the University Staff and was available for any of the Government Staff too.

First thing in the morning reference books for the University lecturers had to be looked out. These were collected by the attendants of the different lecturers and brought back again by them: Dudgeon for Botany I, II, III morphology and taxonomy, Baillie for Malcolm Wilson's classes, and Thompson for Sandy Nelson's physiology classes.

Mr Johnstone normally opened the mail and saw to requests and replies, but I used to check all new books and periodicals for pagination errors etc. Weekly garden papers had to be scanned and items of interest noted and relayed to the staff concerned: Rhododendrons for the Professor and Dr Cowan, Primulas for the Professor and Harold Fletcher, Gentians and Campanulas for David Wilkie. Duplicate gardening papers were kept for press cuttings and these had to be mounted and stored when time allowed. Every week a list came into the Library of plants in flower and these were checked and filed. Papers for Notes from the RBG had to be checked and prepared for printing as also those for the Transactions of the Botanical Society. Afterwards all the exchanges had to be sorted and recorded. Then there were the periodicals chosen for binding, usually during the students' summer vacation, and these had to be checked before and after delivery.

Every summer vacation too, Baillie came with a vacuum cleaner to dust the books and the shelves. Malcolm Wilson always had research students perhaps studying for a Ph.D.: A S Boughey, E O Callen and Mr McMeekan. Dr Lucy Boyd and Dr Bessie Knox also had a room for study from time to time and in the Herbarium were two post-graduate students from India—S K Mukerjee and D K Chatterjee.

Meetings of the Botanical Society and the Royal Society always brought visitors to the Library, which became quite a thrill; Prof. Matthews from Aberdeen, Prof. Graham from St Andrews, Sir D'Arcy Thompson too, Dr Edith Philips Smith from Dundee, Prof. Walton from Glasgow, Robert Scarlett from Inveresk, Sir Harold Stiles, the Surgeon, and Mrs Watt whose son was in the Forestry Commission.

The University Staff and Government Botanists used the library daily. If a Government Botanist helped himself to a book Mr Johnstone would call out 'Looking for?'. If he wanted me to do anything special he would say 'Here's a wee job for you'. He knew his books and their places well too, for on one occasion coming to visit us at home, he immediately spotted two library books in our book-shelves. I suppose they should never have left the RBG but they were returned.

The Library was the centre too for allied Botanical workers. Frequently Dr Wyllie Fenton, Prof. Shearer and Prof. Stebbing from the Agricultural College in George Square would come to consult books. Also the Gregors from Plant Breeding Research; Dr Black and Dr M Noble from East Craigs and frequently Dr Foister and Colin Cadman before he went to Dundee. I suppose these were the Halcyon days of the calm before the storm, because although the Library was in touch with the outside world through correspondence and exchanges, it was very much a little world of its own. We all knew it was really bursting at the seams with more and more books and pamphlets being stored in odd rooms and boxes, but no one seemed to agitate for improvement. Mr Johnstone ran the Library on his own without a supervisory committee. He made the lists for new books and periodicals and had to decide whether they came through the Botanical Society Exchanges or Government vote and these requests went to the Regius Keeper for approval.

When Herbarium specimens and seeds came from a plant hunting expedition all senior helpers were drafted in to help allocate seed packets to various subscribers, Botanic Gardens, plant nurseries or private individuals. Such an occasion arose in 1938 when seeds and plants arrived from Dr Yu in China. Miss Stott skilfully divided the seeds from their bags with a ruler after they had been spread out on the laboratory bench into 20 or 30 lots, depending on the number of subscribers, and we had to packet them. I think there are many plants in the RBG still flourishing as a result of that expedition.

Then came the war. Mr Johnstone asked me to stay on lest he should be sent elsewhere. In World War I he had been trained in an Infantry Division at Fort George, Inverness and then was placed on Home Defence at Deal in Kent. Dr Cowan and Mr Anthony went to the Forestry and Timber Service; and to relieve the Regius Keeper, Harold Fletcher took over teaching of Botany II and III. Miss Stott and I demonstrated to Botany I and the Medicals in the summer term. In the summer afternoons all senior helpers worked outside in the Garden in the Arboretum Department. We trained in First-Aid, in Fire-watching and started a National Savings Group. Dr Nelson and Mr J L S Smith took over all the medical teaching and Botany I.

As far as I remember Harold Fletcher still ran the evening classes for the Workers' Education Association and following Dr Cowan gave broadcasts in Botany for the schools. I used to look up references and prepare a draft script for Dr Cowan and that was fun.

Harold and I were married in December 1941 and I retired for good in 1942.

Appendix VIII

Extract from the typescript of a talk given by Mr W H Brown
on 17 December 1971 at a meeting
of the East of Scotland Branch of the Scottish Library Association,
at the Royal Botanic Garden, Edinburgh.

. . . The buildings we occupied [in 1961] were not greatly different from those Isaac Bayley Balfour had known, only the rooms had been moved around. The most obvious change was perhaps the fact that the Regius Keeper no longer occupied Inverleith House and his office was in the main building instead of the old stable block of what is now the Gallery of Modern Art (in fact its tea-room). To compensate, we had No. 20 Inverleith Row, previously the house of the Ministry of Work's Under Secretary but this was largely a store . . . The library occupied the first floor north wing of the old building on Inverleith Row, a narrow constricted room with bays of shelving about two feet apart and rising some of them to ten feet. In the corridor outside the incomparable illustrations collection was crammed into old herbarium cabinets while the pre-Linnean literature including the great flower books were downstairs in room 6 and 10. There were pockets of books in old personal lockers in the corridor leading to the old lecture hall and some in the former dining-room of 20 Inverleith Row. In these conditions subject classification was impossible and the stock was arranged largely on fixed location. There were some complications. The first was that certain sections of the stock most relevant to the work of the herbarium, the floristic works, were classified by an arrangement devised by a scientific officer who had been in charge of the herbarium. The second was the fact that the library was still the departmental library for botany of the University and its stock came classified from the University and had to be re-classified by this ad hoc system. Worse was to come however for my predecessor Marguerite Allford had begun the re-classification of the entire stock by Bliss so that we had to juggle with no fewer than four systems (a) fixed location (b) the ad hoc system (c) the embryonic Bliss and (d) the University's adaptation of Decimal Classification and none of this as you can imagine lent itself for efficiency. Until 1962 periodical stock was purchased partly by the Government and partly by the University and many of the books in the library were either Botany Department purchases or permanent loans from the main University Library. Students of the Department had free access to the library and had the ordinary borrowing rights of matriculated students, but this led to tremendous difficulties for much of the work of the herbarium depends on certain access to standard works and loans of such material is an embarrassment. Early in 1962, Professor Robert Brown decided that it was time to consolidate the University book and periodical stock into its own room within the old building, and a lecture room was sacrificed for this purpose. The separation of stock was the subject of long discussion between Government and University staff and it was finally agreed that only deposited material recorded in the University would be removed. This was a generous settlement for the Garden because it left in the library a considerable amount of material that had been paid for out of University funds in the days of the earlier professors. Thereafter the library and the Departmental Library developed quite separately and shortly after the separation a departmental librarian was appointed . . . The stages of the separation were the Government's move to its new building in 1964 and a year later the move of the University Department to its own custom-built premises at King's Buildings.

Appendix IX

Extract from Dr H R Fletcher's memorandum to the
Secretary of the Department of Agriculture
and Fisheries for Scotland, in 1969.

The library at the Royal Botanic Garden merits special mention. It is the finest of its kind in Britain outside Kew and the British Museum. Its stock and services are of vital importance for the research being done and advisory services offered at the garden. The library is used not only by the Scientific Staff and horticultural students at the Garden, but also by a number of other organisations and institutions in Scotland and elsewhere, including universities, industrial research organisations and the Botanical Society of Edinburgh. Besides, every year visitors and research workers from this country and from abroad come to use the resources of this library.

The library has a stock of 47,000 books and bound volumes of journals. Some of the pre-Linnean collection of books date back to the first half of the sixteenth century and some others are so scarce that they are priceless possessions jealously guarded. There is also a vast collection of pamphlets and reprints, illustrations and cuttings, photographs and photographic slides, maps, atlases, dictionaries, gazetteers, diaries, correspondence, etc. which add up to well over 200,000 items.

The library is under the immediate charge of a graduate, chartered librarian, assisted by an assistant librarian, one clerical officer, one clerical assistant and a typist. Assistance to the Scientific staff and visitors, enquiries, supervision, indexing, loans, binding, and such other duties leave hardly any time to the librarian or his assistant to attend to the considerable collection of valuable material presently kept in the Store or to undertake any bibliographical research for which there is great scope.

Satisfying the library needs of the Scientific staff should remain the primary purpose of the library; it must, however, be emphasised that this is a national botanical and horticultural library for Scotland, and adequate funds should be made available not only to maintain, but to enhance its stock, services and status as befits a national library.

Appendix X

Notes on a selection of some unique and interesting items in the Library.

References to Arnold Arbor., BM(NH), Dunthorne, EUL, Henrey, Hunt, Lindley, Linnean Soc., Nissen, Pritzel, Sitwell & Blunt, Sotheby, and Stafleu & Cowan refer respectively to:—

ARNOLD ARBORETUM: *Catalogue of the library of the Arnold Arboretum of the Harvard University.* Compiled . . . by Ethelyn Maria Tucker. 2 Vols. Cambridge (Mass.), 1914–1917 [Publication of the Arnold Arboretum No. 6].

BRITISH MUSEUM (NATURAL HISTORY): *Catalogue of the books, manuscripts, maps and drawings in the British Museum (Natural History).* 5 Vols + Vols 6–8 Supplements. London, 1903–1915 + 1922–1940.

DUNTHORNE, Gordon: *Flower and fruit prints of the 18th and early 19th Centuries.* New York, 1970.

EDINBURGH UNIVERSITY LIBRARY: *Catalogue of the printed books in the Library of the University of Edinburgh.* 3 Vols. Edinburgh, 1918–1923.

HENREY, Blanche: *British botanical and horticultural literature before 1800.* 3 Vols. Oxford University Press, 1975.

HUNT BOTANICAL LIBRARY: *Catalogue of the books in the collection of Rachael McMasters Miller Hunt.* 2 Vols in 3. Compiled by Jane Quinby (Vol. 1) & Allan Stevenson (Vol. 2). Pittsburgh, 1958 & 1961.

LINDLEY LIBRARY: *Catalogue of books, pamphlets, manuscripts and drawings.* London, Royal Horticultural Society, 1927.

LINNEAN SOCIETY: *Catalogue of the printed books and pamphlets in the library of the Linnean Society of London.* New edition. London, 1925.

NISSEN, Claus: *Die botanische Buchillustration.* 2 Vols in 1. Stuttgart, 1951. (Supplement, 1966).

PRITZEL, G A: *Thesaurus literaturae botanicae . . .* Editionum novum reformatam. Milano, 1950.

SITWELL, Sacheverell & BLUNT, Wilfrid: *Great flower books . . . 1700–1900.* London, 1956.

SOTHEBY & Co.: *The magnificent botanical library of the Stiftung für Botanik . . . collected by the late Arpad Plesch.* Parts I, II & III. (London, 1975–1976).

STAFLEU, Frans A & COWAN, Richard S: *Taxonomic literature . . .* Second edition. Vol. 1– Utrecht, 1976– (In progress; 5 Vols have been published to the end of 1985).

ATKINS, Anna
[Cyanotype photographs of] *British Algae* 184–? Three vols in two + one loose part and six loose plates. 26×21 cm. (Plate 4).

Vols I & II bound in one, came to the Library in 1888 in the gift of the Director of the Royal Botanic Gardens, Kew. How the others came is not certain. The Edinburgh set is described by Larry Schaff in *History of Photography*, 1982, vol. 6, pp. 166–168.

COOKSON, James (Mrs)
Flowers drawn and painted in India [1835]. 31 interleaved handcoloured plates. Bound in green silk with broad decorated leather spine and front corners. 60×44 cm. Folio. (Plate 5).

There is no date or imprint on the title page. Dunthorne (82) and Nissen (399) give the date of publication as 1830. But from the watermark date 1834 on some of the plates and another copy dated 1835 which they have seen, Sotheby & Co. (Pt. 1, no. 150) have proposed 1835 as the date of publication. Furthermore, this later date is more acceptable because in reply to an enquiry on the book, and more particularly on the artist, Mildred Archer of the India Office Library, London, wrote on 18 June 1964:—

. . . The only James Cookson I can find is George James Cookson (1805–1838) of the Bengal Artillery who was in India from 2 January 1823 until 1838 when he died of smallpox at Karnal (Punjab). He married Catherine Teresa, daughter of P Murray of Co. Wicklow on 8 June 1832. This is the problem, as in 1830 she would not have been Mrs James Cookson although she may have been in India before her marriage and could have made the drawings of Indian flowers . . .

The book was presented to the RBG Library, Edinburgh by Her Majesty Queen Elizabeth II on the occasion of the opening of the new Herbarium and Library building by Her Majesty in 1964.

DALTON, John
Hortus siccus . . . [Vol. 1], 1791 and Vol. 2, 1793. Vol. 1 has title page, 4 pp. of index and 88 pp. of plant specimens; Vol. 2 has title page, 2 pp. of index and 46 pp. of plant specimens. 32×21 cm. (Fig. 17).
  These were assembled by John Dalton, the chemist, for Mr Crosthwaite in Keswick.
Ref.: WOOD, David (1970). *J. Soc. Bibliog. Nat. Hist.* vol. 5, pp. 270–271.

ELIOT, Robert
Hortus siccus. 1702. 164 sheets of plant specimens+one page of Index to plant names. 18 blank sheets at end. 31×22 cm. (Plate 6; Fig. 5).
  Worn original leather binding and pages neatly repaired, retaining much of gilt decorations and tooling on front and back boards and spine. Presented to the University of Edinburgh in 1702 by Robert Eliot, the first Professor of Anatomy there. For information on Eliot *see*:—
RITCHIE, Robert Peel (1899). *The early days of the Royal College of Physicians of Edinburgh.* Edinburgh, p. 28.
SMITH, R W Innes (1932). *English speaking students of Medicine at the University of Leyden.* Edinburgh, pp. 78–79.

FORBES, Edward
'Geology and Flora of the Isle of Man, with recent additions by James F Robinson.' (1831–1834(?). 6 foolscap sheets (4 pp. by Forbes, with a title page, 2 pp. of additional plant records and a letter by Robinson). MS. 32×20 cm. The map on top of p. 1 is illustrated in (Plate 7).
  This manuscript was sent to Prof. John Hutton Balfour in Edinburgh by Robinson with a letter dated 12 December 1881 which reads:—

  I thought the accompanying Fl. of I. of Man, by Prof. Forbes, would have a deep interest for the Botanical Society: you will see it in his own MS. Its history may be briefly narrated. I was working up the Flora carefully, for Mr Watson, my notes were in every instance borne out by Forbes; so that Mr Watson gave me the MS as a keepsake, to make what use of I deemed proper, though I did not think it right to use them publicly, in his lifetime, now however there is not the least reason for keeping it back. It was written about the period when he left the university as a student for Mr Watson's Cybele.
    If you lithograph the map for your Transactions I will gladly do my best to raise you the cost, so that it may be no expense to the Society.
    I should be glad to hear what you can think about it.
    Your truly
  James F Robinson

The *Trans. Proc. Bot. Soc. Edinb.*, 1883, vol. 14, p. cvi records that Forbes' paper was read at their meeting on 12 January 1882 and adds:—

  On the MSS originally prepared for the use of the late Hewett Cottrell Watson in 1839, was a sketch map, coloured to show the lithological divisions of the island as then recognised; and, with this, a brief petrological description. In the accompanying list of plants, to which Mr Robinson had added many species by subsequent researches, the geognostic character of the soils on which they grow is carefully described.

D E Allen has provided the following note on this Forbes MS:—

  Edward Forbes was only the second person to compile a Manx plant list—and his list of which this is the original manuscript, is the only one to have survived. It was the product of his first serious botanising, during his student vacations from Edinburgh

University, in the spring of 1831 and the late summers of 1832 and 1834. Compiled at the request of H C Watson, in whose *New Botanist's Guide* it appeared in 1837, it extends to a respectable 348 species. Though unlocalised, it indicates frequencies and the geological formation(s) on which each had been observed. This is sufficient to make it a datum-line of great value, for no comparable information was to be published on the Island's vascular plants till more than half a century later. Forbes subsequently expanded it and documented it more fully, intending to produce a Flora proper, but changes in his circumstances forced him to leave off and subsequently he allowed his records to be creamed off by various local guides. Watson had meanwhile, however, preserved the 1837 MS version and when a new would-be Flora-writer, J F Robinson of Fordsham in Cheshire appeared on the scene around 1873, willingly passed that over. In the event, though, Robinson did no more than append a few (largely dubious) records of his own before presenting it in 1881 to the Botanical Society of Edinburgh. Unaware of this, Manx scholars had long since despaired of its existence when, almost exactly a century later, it was found to be in the Edinburgh RBG's archives. A copy has been presented to the Manx Museum in view of its exceptional historical interest.

References:

Allen, D E (1983) Watsonia 14: 447

Allen, D E (1984) Flora of the Isle of Man, Douglas, 1984, p.35

GREVILLE, Robert Kaye (1794–1866)

Flora Edinensis: or a description of plants growing near Edinburgh, arranged according to the Linnean System. With a concise introduction to the natural order of the Class Cryptogamia and illustrative plates. Edinburgh, Printed for William Blackwood, Edinburgh; and T Cadell, Strand, London, 18 March 1824. lxxxi+478 pp. 4 plates. 21.5×14 cm.

The RBG Library has Greville's own interleaved copy of pp. 213–471 (Class Cryptogamia) with index pages 472–478 and plates at the back, in which he has written additional notes, descriptions and given coloured drawings.

In his obituary of Greville, John Hutton Balfour said: 'He studied plants before he knew that any book was written on the subject, and before he was nineteen he had made careful coloured drawings of between one and two hundred native plants . . . A few years ago Dr Greville and I commenced a work, which was to be entitled 'Plant Scenery of the World', in which the characteristic floras of different regions were to be represented, and a description was to be given of the plants in the landscape. He completed forty or fifty of the coloured plates, and I prepared some of the letterpress, but owing to the difficulty of getting good coloured lithographs—such at least as were reckoned satisfactory by Dr Greville—it was abandoned by the publishers, Messrs Edmonston & Douglas, who possess the drawings. I still think that the work might be carried on, and that it might prove valuable as illustrating the geographical distribution of plants . . .' (*Trans. Bot. Soc. Edinb.,* 1866, vol. 8, pp. 463–476).

Copies of the advertisement for the 'Plant Scenery of the World', the first two printed pages of text, proofs of three plates and Balfour's own MS notes, etc. on the project are in the RBG Library. The work was to have been completed in about 30 monthly parts at 2s. each.

Also in the RBG Library are some 40 of Greville's original drawings and paintings which came to the Garden in 1920 from Douglas & Foulis who presumably were successors of Edmonston & Douglas. (see frontispiece).

GRISEBACH, August Heinrich Rudolph

La végétation du globe . . . vol. 1. 1875. [i] ii–vii [viii–ix] x–xvi, [1]–765+folded map (col.) at end. 27×17.5 cm.

Stafleu & Cowan (2185) do not mention this vol. 1, published in Paris by L Guerin et Cie, in 1875.

HILL, John

Vegetable system . . . Quarto edition. 1759–1765.

This edition is not mentioned by Henrey or Stafleu & Cowan. Set of eight volumes bound in four, in the library of the Royal Botanic Garden, Edinburgh. 26×19 cm. (Fig. 8).

    [Vol. I]: [i–v] vi–vii [viii] [1] 2–214 [215–216] Pl. 1–21 (1759)

    Vol. II [Part I]: [1–4] [1] 2–121 Pl. 1–36* (1761)

    Vol. II, Part II: 122–211 [212–216] Pl. 37–87 (1761)

    Vol. III: [1–2] 3–108 [109–112] Pl. 87 [bis]–137 (1761)

    Vol. IV: 1–66 [67–68] Pl. 1–46 (1762)

Vol. V: [1–3] 4–88 [89–91] Pl. 1–53 (1763)
Vol. VI: 1–128 [129–132] Pl. 1–62 (1764)
Vol. VII: 1–126 [127–129] Pl. 1–60 (1764)
Vol. VIII: [1] 2–110 [111–114] Pl. 1–60 (1765)
Set of four volumes bound in five, in the Edinburgh University Library. 26×19 cm.
[Vol. I]: [i–v] vi [vii–viii] [1] 2–214 [215–216] Pl. 1–21 (1759)
Vol. II [Part I]: [i] ii–iv [v–vi] [1] 2–121 Pl. 1–36* (1761)
Vol. II, Part II: 122–211 [212–216] Pl. 37–87 (1761)
Vol. III: [1–2] 3–108 [109–111] Pl. 87 [bis]–137 (1761)
Vol. IV: 1–66 [67–68] Pl. 1–46 (1762)

The first four volumes of both sets are mostly the same. Several plates in both sets, some more than others, are smaller in size than the text pages. Vol. II, Part I of both sets has plates no. 17, 26 and 36 twice. The EU set has plate no. 29 also twice, but lacks plate no. 28. Plates are not always bound in at the same places in both sets. Plate no. 7 of vol. I of the EU set is a reverse image of the same plate in the RBG set.

All plates in the RBG set show the relevant volume number nearly always at the bottom left-hand corner. Page references appear at the top left-hand corner of plates in vols. I and II. Vols. III, IV and V have 'page' only on their plates, without a number. Plates in vol. VII have 'P' or 'Pa' only, with numbers on only two. No page references are seen on any plates in vols. VI and VIII. Page numbers, where given, bear no relationship to either the place of the plate in the volume or the page in the volume where the relevant text appears.

Volume numbers and page references have been blocked out wholly or partially on all but a very few of the plates in the EU set.

Relevant volume numbers appear with signatures in all volumes except V and VI which do not give volume numbers with signatures. In vol. IV on p. 1 'Vol. II' appears with signature B, and on p. 5 'Vol. III' with signature C, continuing the same volume number throughout.

The plates in the folio set of the work in the library of the Royal Botanic Garden, Edinburgh have the same numbers as in the quarto set. Page references in the folio set are different from the quarto and do refer to the relevant text.

I am grateful to Mr B L Burtt for the following notes:—

Plates on the octavo set of the work in the library of the Royal Botanic Gardens in Kew have relevant page numbers printed in vols I and II parts I and II; thereafter plates printed with 'Page' at top left-hand corner but number not filled in. No plates with volume numbers until vol. V which has them throughout. Plate 7 of vol. I has fig. 92 on left, as in the EU quarto set. Vol. IV, p. 1 marked at base 'Vol. III' with signature B; p. 9 similarly marked 'Vol. III' with C and so on to M (pp. 81–88); signature N appears without volume number on the index.

The 'odd' volume (see Henrey vol. 3, no. 833, as '[Vol. 6]' "containing the whole Class of Umbrella'd or Umbelliferous PLANS [sic] . . . expence of author, Baldwin, 1764", exactly as might be expected for vol. VI but no volume number on title page. In Vol. VI, on bottom of plates, there are no volume numbers with the signatures. Vol. III title page followed by p. 241, signature 'Vol. II Ii' and so on to p. 364 tailed 'End' of the second volume by index to vol. III.

The title pages and dates of the quarto and the first folio editions correspond. The text is the same in both versions, but the plates of the quarto have been simplified from those of the folio usually by cutting out the habit figure and showing the flower or inflorescence and detached leaf. It seems, then, that Hill commenced his colossal work with the intention of producing a folio, a quarto and an octavo edition simultaneously. No doubt the size was intended to match the pockets of a range of purchasers. The idea did not work. The octavo edition was dropped after six volumes, the quarto after eight. Only the primary work, the folio edition, carried on to complete 26 volumes, to which, as Henrey tells us, an additional volume would have been added but for Hill's death.

Ref.: BURTT, B L (1981). *Boletim da Sociedade Broteriana*, vol. 53 (Second Ser.), pp. 1233–1240.

HOFFMANN, George Francis
Germany's flora . . . Vol. I, 1791 and Vol. II, 1795. 12.5×9 cm. (Fig. 14).
Stafleu & Cowan (2887): 'not seen English edition'.
John Hutton Balfour's name plates are on the inside front cover of both volumes.

LINDSAY, John

Drawing of *Cinchona brachycarpa*, with Latin description. 1784. 32×20 cm. (Fig. 10).

Lindsay wrote in the *Trans. Roy. Soc. Edinb.* 1794, vol. 3, p. 211:—

> The tree was first discovered in November 1784 . . . The better to illustrate my meaning, I sent a drawing of this new plant,* with the frutification, to my late excellent friend Dr Hope, who wrote me he would lay my paper before the Royal Society of Edinburgh. His death happened soon after, and prevented his intentions
>
> . . .
>
> *The drawing alluded to cannot now be found . . .

The drawing is dated '20 August 1784'. Lindsay says in his paper that the tree was discovered in November 1784. He could not have made a drawing and written a description of the plant in August if he discovered it only in November. Probably Lindsay got his dates wrong which is understandable because he was writing ten years after the event.

Hope was not able to do whatever he had in mind with the drawing. When he died in 1786 his family took it away along with all else that could be removed from the Garden. In 1899 Hope's botanical possessions were bequeathed to the Garden and the Cinchona drawing might have been among them.

At the time of his death at least part of Hope's herbarium was left at the University where it lay neglected until 1840 when it was amalgamated with the Herbarium of the Botanical Society of Edinburgh to form the Edinburgh University Herbarium, and eventually in 1864 the whole of the Herbarium was moved to the Garden. It is very likely that the drawing and description were kept with the specimen and came to the Garden from the University, and not from the Hope family. This is more likely because the sheets are embossed with the seal of the Edinburgh University Herbarium.

The drawing and description were discovered in the RBG Library, Edinburgh in 1978.

OPIZ, Philipp Maximilian

Deutschlands cryptogamische Gewachse . . . 1816. 17×11.5 cm. (Fig. 12).

Pritzel 6839; Stafleu & Cowan 7090 had not seen a copy with '1816'.

PARK, Mungo

A bound volume of 57 pages with 53 drawings, mostly coloured, a few incomplete. All except the first two (one, a turtle and the other a bat) are of plants, most of them showing floral parts. 43.5×28.5 cm. (Plate 8).

The volume was in the possession of Thomas Brown who taught botany at the University of Glasgow from 1799 to 1808, and was presented to the RBG Library, Edinburgh in 1893 by his daughter Martha Brown who lived at 8 Albyn Place, Edinburgh.

According to Prof. Joseph Ewan of Tulane University (Louisiana, USA) who examined the plates in 1964, the botanical names pencilled in the lower left-hand corner of the plates are in the hand of A B Lambert whose books and MSS were sold at auction in 1842 and this collection may have been acquired at that sale.

Daniel Oliver of Kew identified and named the plants depicted. Plate 22, in which only the flower and three leaves are coloured, is named *Strophanthus sarmentosus* DC. (*S. senegambiae* A. DC.). On this plate is a note, signed 'MP', which says: 'the fruit, leaves and roots of this shrub when boiled to a consistency is used by the Natives for poisoning their arrows.'

SOWERBY, John Edward

English botany . . . 12 volumes+Supplement to the third edition vols I–IV. 1887–1892. All volumes are published in London by George Bell & Sons. No 'editor' is mentioned on the title pages of vols I, III, IV, V and XII. The rest are 'edited by John T Boswell', except the Supplement which is 'compiled by N E Brown'. See below for further details.

Vols	Contents	Dates	Pagination	Plates
I	Ranunculaceae–Cruciferae	1887	viii, 235	1–161
II	Resedaceae–Sapindaceae	1885	246	CLXII–CCCXXII
III	Leguminiferae and Rosaceae	1886	273	323–490

Vols	Contents	Dates	Pagination	Plates
IV	Lythraceae–Dipsaceae	1886	265 + Errata	491–679
V	Compositae	1888	231	680–860
VI	Campanulaceae–Verbenaceae	1891	213	861–1018
VII	Labiatae–Amaranthaceae	1891	194	1019–1177
VIII	Chenopodiaceae	1883	296 + Errata	MCLXXIX–MCCCLXXXIV
IX	Typhaceae–Liliaceae	1883	239	1385–1545
X	Juncaceae and Cyperaceae	1893	183	1546–1685
XI	Graminaceae	1886	Errata + 216	1686–1824
XII	Cryptogamia	1886	Publisher's note; contents of vols; Errata of vol. 12; 332	1825–1922

Vols	Dates	Pagination	Plates
Suppl Third Edn. Vols. I–IV	1892	VIII Errata; notice; 213, viii	36a, 88 for vol. I, 117a, 188a, 260a, 279a, 435a, 483a (not col.), 484, 484a, 484b, (not col.), 485a, 485b, 488a, 608a (15 in all)

I know of no other set of the third edition with the dates of publication on vols. I–XI as given above. See also: Arnold Arbor. vol. 1, p. 661; BM(NH) vol. 5, pp. 1982 & 2066; Dunthorne no. 291; EUL. vol. 3, p. 711; Henrey nos. 1370, 1371 & 1372; Hunt vol. 2, pt. 2, no. 717; Lindley p. 411; Linnean Soc. p. 723; Nissen nos. 2225, 2226 & 2227; Pritzel no. 8792; Sitwell & Blunt pp. 76–77.

Statistical overview of the Library in 1984.

Holdings	
Number of volumes in stock	106,699
Serial titles held	2,400(c)
Current serial titles received	1,685
Pamphlets and separates	80,000(c)
Archival collection	150,000(c)
Prints, paintings, clippings and photographs	250,000(c)
Bibliographical Records	
General catalogue entries	300,000(c)
Monograph Index entries	12,820
Biographical Index entries	5,720
Index of Herbaria, Botanical Gardens and other institutions	1,910
Ericales bibliography entries	8,803

NOTE: All figures with a (c) suffix are approximations.

Index

Printed in Scotland for H.M.S.O. by Alna Press Ltd, Broxburn.
Dd. 287003/HF4640 C20 10/87 (65992)